THE
2011 CHARLTON
COIN GUIDE
50th EDITION

Dealer's buying prices for
Canadian, Newfoundland and Maritime coinage,
Canadian Medals, Tokens and Paper Money,
United States and World Gold Coinage

by
W. K. Cross

The Charlton Press

Toronto, Ontario • Palm Harbor, Florida

Library and Archives Canada Cataloguing this publication as follows

Charlton, J.E., 1911
    Charlton coin guide

18th- ed.; 1978--
Continues: Charlton J. E., 1911- Coin guide of Canadian, Newfoundland and
    Maritime coinage, ISSN 0701-8223.
ISSN 0706-0459
ISBN 978-0-88968-345-7 (50th edition)

      1. Coins, Canadian—Periodicals.   2. Coins, Canadian--Priices--Periodicals
I. Title.

CJ1864.C5114 18- 1978-   737.4'9'71   C79-030323-X

Printed in Canada
in the Province of Quebec

The Charlton Press

Post Office Box 820, Station Willowdale B
North York, Ontario. M2K 2R1 Canada
Tel: 416-488-1418 Fax: 416-488-4656
Tel: 800-442-6042 Fax: 800-442-1542
www.charltonpress.com; E-mail: chpress@charltonpress.com

3

5

CONTENTS

INDEX OF ADVERTISERS

INTRODUCTION

It is more difficult to obtain old coins in circulation, much more so than it was twenty-five years ago. For the most part silver no longer circulates, since its bullion value now exceeds its face value. Generally speaking, the only pre-1968 coins in circulation are one-cent and five-cent pieces, and these seldom pre-date 1953. Older coins must now be purchased through dealers.

BUYING AND SELLING PRICES

Buying prices are what dealers pay for coins. Selling prices are what dealers charge for coins. Generally, dealers will pay 40% to 60% of their selling price. It should be remembered all dealers will pay according to their needs. They will pay well for what they need immediately, but for those coins for which there is no demand, even if they have a high retail value, they will offer substantially less.

The prices shown in this book represent averages or estimates of buying prices and should serve as a guide in negotiating fair prices when buying or selling. Also a clearer idea of which coins are in demand by collectors and dealers can be developed by studying the guide.

Coins should not be mailed for appraisal unless a written response to an inquiry is received from the dealer. If coins are mailed, then they should be sent by registered mail, insured, accompanied by a list of the coins sent, with a complete return address and return postage.

HANDLING AND CLEANING COINS

Coins should be handled by the edges only. Avoid touching the surfaces. Many collectors have found too late that fingerprints cannot be removed from coins or other metal valuables. Proof and specimen quality coins must be handled with extra care since their high lustre is very fragile.

Inevitably, the question of whether to clean coins or not will arise. Probably the best course to follow is, when in doubt don't, until you have contacted an experienced collector or dealer.

The tarnish on silver coins can be removed, but it will not necessarily raise the value. If the tarnish is very thick, then its removal could leave the coin looking much worse.

Nickel coins seldom require cleaning, and only soap and water are safe since nickel is a fairly active metal. Copper and bronze should not be cleaned by anyone who is not knowledgeable in the chemical properties of these metals and their alloys.

Whatever the metal, abrasives must never be used. There are many polishes on the market which are designed for silverware, copper and brass. These must not be used with coins. The results are disastrous.

HANDLING AND CLEANING PAPER MONEY

Inexperienced collectors should always use great care when handling notes. Notes should be handled as little as possible, since oil and perspiration from one's skin can damage and devalue a note. Care should be taken to ensure that unfolded or uncreased notes remain so, and that even marginal tears or abrasions are avoided. Under no circumstances should one ever wash or otherwise try to clean a note since it is likely that the note's value will be considerably reduced. The same is true for ironing or pressing. It should be avoided.

MINT MARKS

A mint mark is a letter stamped on a coin to designate the mint that produced the coins.

Canadian decimal coinage issued prior to 1908 was struck at either the Tower Mint, London, in which case it has no mint mark, or at the Heaton Mint in Birmingham. The Birmingham coins have a small "H" as a mint mark. Since 1908 all Canadian coins have been struck at the Ottawa or Winnipeg Mints, with no mint marks, except the Canadian sovereigns which were identified by a small "C" above the date and a "W" when struck at Winnipeg. Newfoundland's coinage was struck at either London, Birmingham, or Ottawa. The Tower Mint coins had no marks, the Birmingham coins had an "H," and the Ottawa coins had a "C," except for the 1940 and 1942 cent pieces.

The coinage of New Brunswick and Nova Scotia had no mint marks because it was struck at the Tower Mint. Prince Edward Island's coinage was struck at Birmingham, but no mint mark was used because the dies were supplied by the Tower Mint.

COMPOSITION MARKS

Beginning in 1999, the Royal Canadian Mint, after years of development began issuing multiply plated steel coinage. Coins made by this new method carry the letter "P," for plated, on the obverse below the Queen's portrait.

ROYAL CANADIAN MINT LOGO

During mid-2006 the "P" composition mark was replaced by the Royal Canadian Mint logo.

COINS OF CANADA

NOVA SCOTIA

NEW BRUNSWICK

VICTORIA 1861 - 1864

Date and Denomination	Buying Price
1861 half cent	3.00
1864 half cent	3.00
1861 one cent	1.75
1862 one cent	30.00
1864 one cent	1.75

PRINCE EDWARD ISLAND

VICTORIA 1871

Date and Denomination	Buying Price
1871 one cent	1.75

VICTORIA 1861 - 1864

Date and Denomination	Buying Price
1861 half cent	75.00
1861 one cent	2.00
1864 one cent	2.00
1862 five cents	35.00
1864 five cents	35.00
1862 ten cents	35.00
1864 ten cents	45.00
1862 twenty cents	15.00
1864 twenty cents	20.00

IMPORTANT: Buying prices are listed for coins graded VG or better. Bent, damaged or badly worn coins are not collectable and bring no premium value.

NEWFOUNDLAND

LARGE CENTS

Wide 0   Narrow 0

GEORGE V 1913 - 1936

Date and Mint Mark	Buying Price
1913	.50
1917C	.50
1919C	.50
1920C	.50
1929	.50
1936	.50

VICTORIA 1865 - 1896

Date and Mint Mark	Description	Buying Price
1865		2.00
1872H		1.75
1873		2.00
1876H		2.00
1880	Wide 0	1.75
1880	Narrow 0	75.00
1885		15.00
1888		15.00
1890		1.75
1894		1.75
1896		1.75

SMALL CENTS

GEORGE VI 1938 - 1947

Date and Mint Mark	Description	Buying Price
1938		.20
1940		.20
1940	Re-engraved Date	15.00
1941C		.20
1942		.15
1943C		.15
1944C		.15
1947C		.15

EDWARD VII 1904 - 1909

Date and Mint Mark	Buying Price
1904H	3.00
1907	1.25
1909	1.25

FIVE CENTS

VICTORIA 1865 - 1880

Date and Mint Mark	Buying Price
1865	20.00
1870	35.00
1872H	30.00
1873	75.00
1873H	450.00
1876H	75.00
1880	30.00

VICTORIA 1881 - 1896

Date and Mint Mark	Buying Price
1881	25.00
1882H	15.00
1885	85.00
1888	30.00
1890	7.00
1894	5.00
1896	3.00

EDWARD VII 1903 - 1908

Date and Mint Mark	Buying Price
1903	2.00
1904H	1.00
1908	1.00

GEORGE V 1912 - 1929

Date and Mint Mark	Buying Price
1912	1.00
1917C	1.00
1919C	2.00
1929	1.00

GEORGE VI 1938 - 1947

Date and Mint Mark	Buying Price
1938	.60
1940C	.60
1941C	.60
1942C	.60
1943C	.60
1944C	.60
1945C	.60
1946C	200.00
1947C	.60

TEN CENTS

VICTORIA 1865 - 1896

Date and Mint Mark	Buying Price
1865	15.00
1870	100.00
1872H	10.00
1873	25.00
1876H	30.00
1880	30.00
1882H	20.00
1885	55.00
1888	25.00
1890	5.00
1894	5.00
1896	5.00

EDWARD VII 1903 - 1904

Date and Mint Mark	Buying Price
1903	2.00
1904H	.80

GEORGE V 1912 -1919

Date and Mint Mark	Buying Price
1912	.80
1917C	.80
1919C	.80

IMPORTANT: Buying prices are listed for coins graded VG or better. Bent, damaged or badly worn coins are not collectable and bring no premium value.

GEORGE VI 1938 - 1947

Date and Mint Mark	Buying Price
1938	.80
1940	.80
1941C	.80
1942C	.80
1943C	.80
1944C	.80
1945C	.80
1946C	.80
1947C	.80

TWENTY CENTS

VICTORIA 1865 - 1900

Date and Mint Mark	Buying Price
1865	9.00
1870	10.00
1872H	7.00
1873	15.00
1876H	15.00
1880	15.00
1881	8.00
1882H	5.00
1885	8.00
1888	5.00
1890	5.00
1894	5.00
1896	5.00
1899	3.00
1900	3.00

EDWARD VII 1904

Date and Mint Mark	Buying Price
1904H	5.00

GEORGE V 1912

Date and Mint Mark	Buying Price
1912	1.60

TWENTY-FIVE CENTS

GEORGE V 1917 - 1919

Date and Mint Mark	Buying Price
1917C	2.00
1919C	2.00

IMPORTANT: A mint mark is a letter stamped on a coin to designate the mint that produced the coin. The Canadian Mint used the letter "C" or "W," while the Heaton Mint in England used the letter "H."

IMPORTANT: Buying prices listed are for coins graded VG or better. Bent, damaged or badly worn coins are not collectable and bring no premium over the silver value.

FIFTY CENTS

VICTORIA 1870 - 1900

Date and Mint Mark	Buying Price
1870	10.00
1872H	8.00
1873	25.00
1874	15.00
1876H	20.00
1880	16.00
1881	12.00
1882H	8.00
1885	15.00
1888	20.00
1894	7.00
1896	5.00
1898	5.00
1899	5.00
1900	5.00

GEORGE V 1911 - 1919

Date and Mint Mark	Buying Price
1911	4.00
1917C	4.00
1918C	4.00
1919C	4.00

TWO DOLLARS GOLD

VICTORIA 1865 - 1888

Date and Mint Mark	Buying Price
1865	175.00
1870	175.00
1872	200.00
1880	700.00
1881	150.00
1882H	150.00
1885	150.00
1888	150.00

EDWARD VII 1904 - 1909

Date and Mint Mark	Buying Price
1904H	4.00
1907	4.00
1908	4.00
1909	4.00

Note: Two dollar gold coins must be VF condition or better. Damaged, bent or holed coins are bought for gold content.

PROVINCE OF CANADA

LARGE CENTS

Wide 9 over 8　　　　Narrow 9

VICTORIA 1858 - 1859

Date and Mint Mark	Description	Buying Price
1858		30.00
1859	Narrow 9	2.00
1859	* Brass N9	3,500.00
1859	W/9 over 8	15.00

FIVE CENTS

Large date　　　　Small date

VICTORIA 1858

Date and Mint Mark	Description	Buying Price
1858	Small Date	12.50
1858	Large Date	75.00

TEN CENTS

VICTORIA 1858

Date and Mint Mark		Buying Price
1858		15.00
1858 First 8/5		500.00

Note: * Brass metal is yellow in colour.

TWENTY CENTS

VICTORIA 1858

Date and Mint Mark	Buying Price
1858	50.00

CANADA

LARGE CENTS

 Small date Small leaves　　 Large date Large leaves

VICTORIA 1876 - 1901

Date and Mint Mark	Description	Buying Price
1876H		2.00
1881H		3.50
1882H		3.50
1884		2.50
1886		4.00
1887		2.50
1888		2.50
1890H		5.00
1891	Large Leaves, Large Date	5.00
1891	Large Leaves, Small Date	35.00
1891	Small Leaves, Small Date	25.00
1892		4.00
1893		2.00
1894		7.50
1895		4.00
1896		2.50
1897		2.50
1898H		5.00
1899		2.50
1900		5.00
1900H		2.00
1901		2.00

1936 Dot

EDWARD VII 1902 - 1910

Date and Mint Mark	Buying Price
1902	1.00
1903	1.00
1904	1.00
1905	1.00
1906	1.00
1907	1.00
1907H	5.00
1908	1.00
1909	1.00
1910	1.00

GEORGE V 1920 - 1936

Date and Mint Mark	Description	Buying Price
1920		.05
1921		.05
1922		7.00
1923		10.00
1924		3.00
1925		10.00
1926		1.25
1927		.05
1928		.05
1929		.05
1930		1.00
1931		.10
1932		.05
1933		.05
1934		.05
1935		.05
1936		.05
1936	Dot	100,000.00

Note: The 1936 Dot one cent coin is very rare, only three are confirmed. Examples must be authenticated and certified as counterfiet examples do exist.

GEORGE V 1911 - 1920

Date and Mint Mark	Buying Price
1911	.15
1912	.15
1913	.15
1914	.15
1915	.15
1916	.15
1917	.15
1918	.15
1919	.15
1920	.15

GEORGE VI 1937 - 1947

1947 Maple Leaf Blunt 7   1947 Maple Leaf Pointed 7

Date and Mint Mark	Description	Buying Price
1937 to 1947		.01
1947	Maple Leaf, Blunt 7	.10
1947	Maple Leaf, Pointed 7	.01

SMALL CENTS

"A" points to denticles	"A" points between denticles

GEORGE VI 1948 - 1952

Date and Mint Mark	Description	Buying Price
1948	"A" Points to	.01
1948	"A" Between	.10
1949	"A" Points to	2.00
1949	"A" Between	.01
1950 to 1952		.01

No shoulder fold	Shoulder Fold

ELIZABETH II, LAUREATED PORTRAIT, 1953 - 1964

Date and Mint Mark	Description	Buying Price
1953	NSF	.01
1953	SF	.01
1954	SF	.01
1955	NSF	40.00
1955	SF	.01
1956 to 1964		.01

Note: You must sort and identify your own coins. Do not expect a dealer to spend hours sorting them for you.

Centennial

ELIZABETH II, TIARA PORTRAIT, 1965 - 1981

Date and Mint Mark	Description	Buying Price
1965 to 1966		.01
1967	Centennial	.01
1968 to 1981		.01

Blunt 5	Pointed 5

ELIZABETH II, TIARA PORTRAIT, 1982 - 1989

Date and Mint Mark	Description	Buying Price
1982 to 1984		.01
1985	Blunt 5	.01
1985	Pointed 5	1.00
1986 to 1989		.01

1867 - 1992

ELIZABETH II, DIADEMED PORTRAIT, 1990 - 1996

Date and Mint Mark	Description	Buying Price
1990 to 1991		.01
1867-1992	Double Date	.01
1993 to 1996		.01

ELIZABETH II, DIADEMED PORTRAIT, COPPER PLATED ZINC, 1997 - 2003

Date and Mint Mark	Description	Buying Price
1997 to 2001		.01
1952-2002	Double Date	.01
2003		.01

ELIZABETH II, UNCROWNED PORTRAIT, COPPER PLATED ZINC, 2003 - 2006

Date and Mint Mark	Buying Price
2003	.01
2004	.01
2005	.01
2006	.01

 Royal Canadian Mint Logo

ELIZABETH II, UNCROWNED PORTRAIT, COPPER PLATED ZINC, LOGO, 2006 - 2010

Date and Mint Mark	Buying Price
2006-2007	.01
2009	.01
2010	.01

 Composition Mark

ELIZABETH II, DIADEMED PORTRAIT, COPPER PLATED STEEL, 1999P - 2003P

Date and Mint Mark	Description	Buying Price
1999P		2.50
2000P		1,000.00
2001P		.01
1952-2002P	Double Date	.01
2003P		.01

ELIZABETH II, UNCROWNED PORTRAIT, COPPER PLATED STEEL, 2003P - 2006P

Date and Mint Mark	Buying Price
2003P	.01
2004P	.01
2005P	.01
2006P	.01

ELIZABETH II, UNCROWNED PORTRAIT, COPPER PLATED STEEL, LOGO, 2006 - 2010

Date and Mint Mark	Buying Price
2006-2010	.01

Note: 1. The 2000P one cent was issued to vending companies for test purposes.
2. Copper plated steel cents are magnetic, while the copper plated zinc cents are not.

FIVE CENTS SILVER

  Small H   Large H

1874 Plain 4   1874 Crosslet 4

 Small 8   Large 8

1875 1875H Small date Short top on 5   1875 1875H Large date Long top on 5

 Maple   Holly

1900 1900 Small Date   1900 1900 Large Date

EDWARD VII 1902 - 1910

Date and Mint Mark	Description	Buying Price
1902	Plain	1.25
1902	Large H	1.00
1902	Small H	3.00
1903H	Large H	5.00
1903H	Small H	1.25
1903		2.00
1904		1.00
1905		1.00
1906		1.00
1907		1.00
1908	Small 8	3.00
1908	Large 8	20.00
1909	Maple Leaves	1.00
1909	Holly Leaves	6.00
1910	Maple Leaves	6.00
1910	Holly Leaves	1.00

VICTORIA 1870 - 1901

Date and Mint Mark	Description	Buying Price
1870		10.00
1871		10.00
1872H		8.00
1874H	Plain 4	12.00
1874H	Crosslet 4	10.00
1875H	Small Date	75.00
1875H	Large Date	150.00
1880H		10.00
1881H		7.00
1882H		8.00
1883H		10.00
1884		65.00
1885		8.00
1886		7.50
1887		10.00
1888		5.00
1889		10.00
1890H		6.00
1891		5.00
1892		6.00
1893		5.00
1894		10.00
1896		4.00
1897		5.00
1898		5.00
1899		4.00
1900	Large Date	10.00
1900	Small Date	4.00
1901		4.00

GEORGE V 1911 - 1921

Date and Mint Mark	Buying Price
1911	1.00
1912	1.00
1913	1.00
1914	1.00
1915	5.00
1916	1.00
1917	1.00
1918	1.00
1919	1.00
1920	1.00
1921	2,000.00

Note: Buying prices are for coins in **Very Good (VG)** condition.

FIVE CENTS NICKEL

Near 6   Far 6

GEORGE V 1922 - 1936

Date and Mint Mark	Description	Buying Price
1922 to 1924		.10
1925		45.00
1926	Near 6	1.00
1926	Far 6	85.00
1927 to 1936		.10

Tombac Beaver   Tombac "V"

1947 Maple Leaf   1947 Dot

GEORGE VI 1937 - 1947

Date and Mint Mark	Description	Buying Price
1937	Dot	.05
1938 to 1941		.05
1942	Nickel	.05
1942	Tombac Beaver	.15
1943	Tombac V	.05
1944	Tombac V *	10,000.00
1944 to 1945	Steel V	.05
1946 to 1947		.05
1947	Maple Leaf	.05
1947	Dot	10.00

Geo. VI Obverse   Beaver

1951 High Relief   1951 Comm.

A in GRATIA
points to a rim
denticle

A in GRATIA
points between
rim denticles

GEORGE VI 1948 - 1952

Date and Mint Mark	Description	Buying Price
1948	Without "ET IND:IMP"	.05
1949 to 1951		.05
1951	Commemorative	.05
1951	High Relief	200.00
1952		.05

No Shoulder Fold
On the obverse note
the flared ends of "I"
and the closed top of
the "E"

Shoulder Fold
On the obverse note
the straight-sided "I"
and the open top the
the "E"

Note: * This 1944 five cent coin is made of the alloy Tombac. It is brassy in colour when new, and brown when used. It is not the common steel composition of 1944.

| Far Maple Leaf | Near Maple Leaf |

ELIZABETH II, LAUREATED PORTRAIT, 1953 - 1962

Date and Mint Mark	Description	Buying Price
1953	NSF, far	.05
1953	NSF, near	150.00
1953	SF, near	.05
1953	SF. far	75.00
1954	NSF	3,000.00
1954SF to 1962		.05

1964 Extra Water Line

ELIZABETH II, LAUREATED PORTRAIT, 1963 - 1964

Date and Mint Mark	Description	Buying Price
1963 to 1964		.05
1964	Extra Water Line	3.00

| 1965 Small Beads Attached Jewel | 1965 Large Beads Detached Jewel |

ELIZABETH II, TIARA PORTRAIT, 1965 - 1966

Date and Mint Mark	Description	Buying Price
1965	Small Beads	.05
1965	Large Beads	25.00
1966		.05

ELIZABETH II, TIARA PORTRAIT, 1967 - 1989

Date and Mint Mark	Description	Buying Price
1967	Centennial	.05
1968 to 1989		.05

1867-1992

| 5¢ 1996 Far 6 "6" Far from"D" in Canada | 5¢ 1996 Near 6 "6" Near "D" in Canada |

ELIZABETH II, DIADEMED PORTRAIT, CUPRO NICKEL,1990 - 2001

Date and Mint Mark	Description	Buying Price
1990		.05
1991		.05
1867-1992	Double Date	.05
1993-1995		.05
1996	Far 6	.05
1996	Near 6	.05
1997-2001		.05

Note: The price of nickel collapsed in 2009, removing all premium on the 5-cent nickel coinage.

Composition
Mark

ELIZABETH II, UNCROWNED PORTRAIT, CUPRO NICKEL, 2006

Date and Mint Mark	Description	Buying Price
2006		.05

Double dates 1952 2002P

ELIZABETH II, DIADEMED PORTRAIT, NICKEL PLATED STEEL, 1999P - 2003P

Date and Mint Mark	Description	Buying Price
1999P	Issued For Testing	5.00
2000P		.10
2001P		.05
1952-2002P	Double Date	.05
2003P		.05

Royal
Canadian
Mint Logo

ELIZABETH II, UNCROWNED PORTRAIT, NICKEL PLATED STEEL, LOGO, 2006 - 2010

Date and Mint Mark	Description	Buying Price
2006 to 2010	Beaver	.05

Victory
1945-2005

ELIZABETH II, UNCROWNED PORTRAIT, NICKEL PLATED STEEL, 2003P - 2006P

Date and Mint Mark	Description	Buying Price
2003-2005P	Beaver	.05
2005P	Victory, 1945-2005	.05
2006P	Beaver	.05

Note: The nickel plated steel coins are magnetic.

TEN CENTS

1870 Narrow "0"
Sides of equal thickness

1870 Wide "0"
Right side is thicker

1886 Small 6

1886 Large,
Pointed 6

1886 Large,
Knobbed 6

1892
2 over 1
Large 9

1892
Normal Date
Small 9

1893
Flat-top 3
Medium 9

1893
Round-top 3
Large 9

1899
Small 9s

1899
Large 9s

VICTORIA 1870 -1901

Date and Mint Mark	Description	Buying Price
1870	Narrow 0	12.00
1870	Wide 0	18.00
1871		18.00
1871H		18.00
1872H		75.00
1874H		10.00
1875H		200.00

VICTORIA 1870 - 1901 (cont.)

Date and Mint Mark	Description	Buying Price
1880H		10.00
1881H		12.00
1882H		12.00
1883H		35.00
1884		150.00
1885		30.00
1886	Small 6	25.00
1886	Large pointed 6	75.00
1886	Large knobbed 6	25.00
1887		35.00
1888		8.00
1889		500.00
1890H		12.00
1891		12.00
1892	Large 9	150.00
1892	Small 9	12.00
1893	Flat Top 3	25.00
1893	Round Top 3	500.00
1894		20.00
1896		8.00
1898		6.00
1899	Small 9	8.00
1899	Large 9	12.00
1900		6.00
1901		5.00

EDWARD VII 1902 - 1910

Date and Mint Mark	Description	Buying Price
1902		3.00
1902H		3.00
1903		5.00
1903H		3.00
1904		5.00
1905		3.00
1906		3.00
1907		3.00
1908		5.00
1909	Victorian Leaves	3.00
1909	Broad Leaves	5.00
1910		3.00

Note: Buying prices are for coins in **Very Good (VG)** condition. Coins of lower grades will be bought at lower prices.

Small Leaves	Broad leaves

1969 Small Date	1969 Large Date

GEORGE V 1911 - 1936

Date and Mint Mark	Description	Buying Price
1911		3.00
1912		1.00
1913	Small Leaves	1.00
1913	Broad Leaves	40.00
1914 to 1936		.70

GEORGE VI 1937 - 1947

Date and Mint Mark	Description	Buying Price
1937 to 1947		.70
1947	Maple Leaf	.70

GEORGE VI 1948 - 1952

Date and Mint Mark	Description	Buying Price
1948	Without "ET IND"IMP"	.70
1949 to 1952		.70

ELIZABETH II, LAUREATED PORTRAIT, 1953 - 1964

Date and Mint Mark	Buying Price
1953 to 1964	.70

1980 Wide 0	1980 Narrow 0

ELIZABETH II, TIARA PORTRAIT, 1965 - 1989

Date and Mint Mark	Description	Buying Price
1965 to 1966		.70
1967	Centennial	.55
1968	.500 Fine Silver	.40
1968	Nickel	.10
1969	Large Date	6,500.00
1969	Small Date	.10
1970 to 1979		.10
1980	Wide 0	3.00
1980	Narrow 0	.10
1981 to 1989		.10

1867-1992

ELIZABETH II, DIADEMED PORTRAIT, 1990 - 2000

Date and Mint Mark	Description	Buying Price
1990 to 1991		.10
1992	Double Date	.10
1993 to 2000		.10

Composition Mark

Royal Canadian Mint Logo

Year of the Volunteer

ELIZABETH II, UNCROWNED PORTRAIT, NICKEL PLATED STEEL, LOGO, 2006 - 2010

Date and Mint Mark	Buying Price
2006	.10
2007	.10
2008	.10
2009	.10
2010	.10

Double dates 1952 2002P

ELIZABETH II, DIADEMED PORTRAIT, NICKEL PLATED STEEL, 1999P - 2003P

Date and Mint Mark	Description	Buying Price
1999P		2.50
2000P		400.00
2001P	Volunteers	.10
2001P	Bluenose	.10
1952-2002P	Double Date	.10
2003P		.10

ELIZABETH II, UNCROWNED PORTRAIT, NICKEL PLATED STEEL, 2003P - 2006P

Date and Mint Mark	Buying Price
2003P	.10
2004P	.10
2005P	.10
2006P	.10

TWENTY-FIVE CENTS

Narrow 0   Wide 0

Small crown   Large crown

6 over 7   6 over 6

EDWARD VII 1902 - 1910

Date and Mint Mark	Description	Buying Price
1902		7.00
1902H		5.00
1903		7.00
1904		9.00
1905		6.00
1906	Small Crown	750.00
1906	Large Crown	3.00
1907		4.00
1908		5.00
1909		3.00
1910		3.00

VICTORIA 1870 - 1901

Date and Mint Mark	Description	Buying Price
1870		15.00
1871		20.00
1871H		18.00
1872H		10.00
1874H		10.00
1875H		300.00
1880H	Narrow O	30.00
1880H	Wide O	85.00
1881H		15.00
1882H		22.00
1883H		15.00
1885		100.00
1886		60.00
1886	6 over 7	60.00
1886	6 over 6	75.00
1887		90.00
1888		20.00
1889		125.00
1890H		15.00
1891		50.00
1892		15.00
1893		75.00
1894		22.50
1899		10.00
1900		70.00
1901		7.00

GEORGE V 1911 - 1936

Date and Mint Mark	Description	Buying Price
1911		5.00
1912 to 1914		1.75
1915		8.00
1916 to 1920		1.75
1921		5.00
1927		15.00
1928 to 1936		1.75
1936	Dot	15.00

Note: Buying prices are for coins in **Very Good (VG)** condition. Coins with excessive wear, holed or bent will be discounted from the listed price.

1947 Dot	1947 Maple Leaf

GEORGE VI 1937 - 1947

Date and Mint Mark	Description	Buying Price
1937 to 1947		1.75
1947	Maple Leaf	1.75
1947	Dot	20.00

Centennial	RCMP

1973 Small Bust	1973 Large Bust
120 Obverse Beads	132 Obverse Beads
Far from Rim	Near Rim

GEORGE VI 1948 - 1952

Date and Mint Mark	Descripton	Buying Price
1948	Without "ET IND:IMP"	1.75
1949 to 1952		1.75

ELIZABETH II, TIARA PORTRAIT, 1965 - 1973

Date and Mint Mark	Description	Buying Price
1965 to 1966		1.75
1967	Centennial	1.40
1968	.500 Fine Silver	1.00
1968 to 1972	Nickel	.25
1973	Small Bust	.25
1973	Large Bust	60.00

ELIZABETH II, LAUREATED PORTRAIT, 1953 - 1964

Date and Mint Mark	Description	Buying Price
1953	Large Date	1.75
1953	Small Date	1.75
1954 to 1964		1.75

ELIZABETH II, TIARA PORTRAIT, 1974 - 1989

Date and Mint Mark	Buying Price
1974 to 1989	.25

Note: Victoria, Edward and George V quarters must be **Very Good (VG)** or better.

ELIZABETH II, DIADEMED PORTRAIT, 1990 - 1991

Date and Mint Mark	Buying Price
1990	.25
1991	1.00

CANADA 125 ANNIVERSARY

Common Obverse

New Brunswick   Northwest Territories

Newfoundland   Manitoba

Yukon   Alberta

Prince Edward Island   Ontario

Nova Scotia   Quebec

Saskatchewan   British Columbia

ELIZABETH II, DIADEMED PORTRAIT, 1992

Date and Mint Mark	Description	Buying Price
1992	New Brunswick	.25
1992	Northwest Territories	.25
1992	Newfoundland	.25
1992	Manitoba	.25
1992	Yukon	.25
1992	Alberta	.25
1992	Prince Edward Island	.25
1992	Ontario	.25
1992	Nova Scotia	.25
1992	Quebec	.25
1992	Saskatchewan	.25
1992	British Columbia	.25

ELIZABETH II, DIADEMED PORTRAIT, 1993 - 2001

Date and Mint Mark	Description	Buying Price
1993 to 1996		.25
2001		.25

1999 MILLENNIUM QUARTERS

Common Obverse

November　　　December

ELIZABETH II, DIADEMED PORTRAIT, 1999

Date and Mint Mark	Description	Buying Price
1999	January	.25
1999	February	.25
1999	March	.25
1999	April	.25
1999	May	.25
1999	June	.25
1999	July	.25
1999	August	.25
1999	September	.25
1999	October	.25
1999	November	.25
1999	December	.25

January　　　February

March　　　April

May　　　June

July　　　August

September　　　October

2000 MILLENNIUM QUARTERS

Common Obverse

January　　　February

March　　　April

May | June

July | August

September | October

November | December

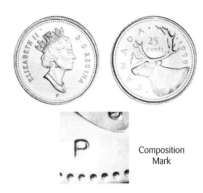

P

Composition
Mark

ELIZABETH II, DIADEMED PORTRAIT, NICKEL PLATED STEEL, 1999P - 2001P

Date and Mint Mark	Buying Price
1999P	5.00
2000P	5,000.00
2001P	.25

ELIZABETH II, DIADEMED PORTRAIT, NICKEL PLATED STEEL, 2002P - 2003P

Date and Mint Mark	Description	Buying Price
1952-2002P	Canada Day, Double Date	.25
1952-2002P	Caribou, Double Date	.25
2003P		.25

ELIZABETH II, DIADEMED PORTRAIT, 2000

Date and Mint Mark	Description	Buying Price
2000	January, Pride	.25
2000	February, Ingenuity	.25
2000	March, Achievement	.25
2000	April, Health	.25
2000	May, Natural Legacy	.25
2000	June, Harmony	.25
2000	July, Celebration	.25
2000	August, Family	.25
2000	September, Wisdom	.25
2000	October. Creativity	.25
2000	November, Freedom	.25
2000	December, Community	.25

First Settlement
2004 | Poppy 2004

Note: If a date is not listed then it was not issed for circulation.

Alberta
2005

Saskatchewan
2005

Year of the Veteran
2006

Breast Cancer
2006

ELIZABETH II, UNCROWNED PORTRAIT, NICKEL PLATED STEEL, 2003P - 2006P

Date and Mint Mark	Description	Buying Price
2003P	Caribou	.25
2004P	Caribou	.25
2004P	First Settlement	.25
2004P	Poppy	.25
2005P	Caribou	.25
2005P	Alberta	.25
2005P	Saskatchewan	.25
2005P	Year of the Veteran	.25
2006P	Caribou	.25
2006P	Breast Cancer	.25

Medal of Bravery

Royal
Canadian
Mint Logo

ELIZABETH II, UNCROWNED PORTRAIT, LOGO, NICKEL PLATED STEEL, 2006 - 2010

Date and Mint Mark	Description	Buying Price
2006	Caribou	.25
2006	Medal of Bravery	.25
2007	Caribou	.25
2008	Caribou	.25
2009	Caribou	.25
2010	Caribou	.25

VANCOUVER 2010 PARALYMPIC WINTER GAMES

2007 Obv.
Paralympic Games

Wheelchair Curling

2007 Vancouver Logo

Wheelchair Curling
Mule

2009 Obv.
Paralympic Games

Ice Sledge Hockey

ELIZABETH II, UNCROWNED PORTRAIT, NICKEL PLATED STEEL, 2007 - 2009

Date and Mint Mark	Description	Buying Price
2007	Wheelchair Curling	.25
2007	Mule	50.00
2009	Ice Sledge Hockey	.25

Note: The Wheelchair Curling Mule is found only in the uncirculated sets of 2007.

VANCOUVER 2010 WINTER OLYMPIC GAMES

Olympic Obv.

Curling

Ice Hockey

Biathlon

Alpine Skiing

Snowboarding

Freestyle Skiing

Figure Skating

Bobsleigh

Speed Skating

Cross Country Skiing

VANCOUVER 2010 WINTER OLYMPIC GAMES GOLDEN MOMENTS

Men's Ice Hockey 'Standard'

Men's Ice Hockey 'Colourised'

Raised 2

Incused 2

Reverse date 2002

Women's Ice Hockey 'Standard'

Women's Ice Hockey 'Colourised'

Cindy Klassen 'Standard'

Cindy Klassen 'Colourised'

ELIZABETH II, UNCROWNED PORTRAIT, NICKEL PLATED STEEL, 2007 - 2009

Date and Mint Mark	Description	Buying Price
2007	Curling	.25
2007	Ice Hockey	.25
2007	Biathlon	.25
2007	Alpine Skiing	.25
2008	Snowboarding	.25
2008	Freestyle Skiing	.25
2008	Figure Skating	.25
2008	Bobsleigh	.25
2009	Speed Skating	.25
2009	Cross Country Skiing	.25

ELIZABETH II, UNCROWNED PORTRAIT, NICKEL PLATED STEEL, 2009

Date and Mint Mark	Description	Buying Price
2009	Men's Hockey, Raised 2	.25
2009	Men's Hockey, Colourised, Raised 2	25
2009	Men's Hockey, Colourised, Incused 2	.25
2009	Women's Hockey	.25
2009	Women's Hockey, Colourised	.25
2009	Cindy Klassen	.25
2009	Cindy Klassen, Colourised	.25

FIFTY CENTS

L.C.W.   No L.C.W.

VICTORIA 1870 - 1901

Date and Mint Mark	Description	Buying Price
1870	Without L.C.W.	650.00
1870	With L.C.W.	30.00
1871		30.00
1871H		85.00
1872H		35.00
1881H		30.00
1888		175.00
1890H		750.00
1892		60.00
1894		250.00
1898		40.00
1899		125.00
1900		30.00
1901		35.00

EDWARD VII 1902 - 1910

Date and Mint Mark	Description	Buying Price
1902		10.00
1903H		25.00
1904		60.00
1905		65.00
1906		8.00
1907		6.00
1908		8.00
1909		8.00
1910	Victorian Leaves	8.00
1910	Edwardian Leaves	6.00

GEORGE V 1911 - 1936

Date and Mint Mark	Description	Buying Price
1911		10.00
1912		4.00
1913		4.00
1914		10.00
1916		4.00
1917		4.00
1918		4.00
1919		4.00
1920	Wide 0	3.50
1920	Narrow 0	3.50
1921		16,000.00
1929		3.00
1931		7.00
1932		60.00
1934		9.00
1936		9.00

Straight "7"   Curved "7"
No Maple Leaf   No Maple Leaf

Straight "7"   Curved "7"
With Maple Leaf   With Maple Leaf

Note: Coins must grade **Very Good** or better. Badly worn coins (good) will be priced lower.

GEORGE VI 1937 - 1947

Date and Mint Mark	Description	Buying Price
1937 to 1946		3.50
1947	Straight "7"	3.50
1947	Curved "7"	3.50
1947	M.L., Straight "7"	10.00
1947	M.L., Curved "7"	800.00

GEORGE VI 1948 - 1952

Date and Mint Mark	Description	Buying Price
1948	Without "ET IND:IMP"	45.00
1949 to 1952		3.50

No shoulder fold   Shoulder fold

Small date   Large date

ELIZABETH II, LAUREATED PORTRAIT, 1953 - 1964

Date and Mint Mark	Description	Buying Price
1953	NSF, SD	3.50
1953	NSF, LD	3.50
1953	SF, LD	3.50
1954 to 1964		3.50

ELIZABETH II, TIARA PORTRAIT, 1965 - 1967

Date and Mint Mark	Description	Buying Price
1965 to 1966		3.50
1967	Centennial	3.50

1978 Square Jewels

1978 Round Jewels

1982 - 118 Large Beads

1982 - 120 Small beads

ELIZABETH II, TIARA PORTRAIT, 1968 - 1989

Date and Mint Mark	Description	Buying Price
1968 to 1977		.50
1978	Square Jewels	.50
1978	Round Jewels	1.00
1979 to 1981		.50
1982	Large Beads	.50
1982	Small Beads	10.00
1983 to 1989		.50

ELIZABETH II, DIADEMED PORTRAIT, 1990 - 2000

Date and Mint Mark	Description	Buying Price
1990 to 1991		.50
1867-1992	Double Date	.50
1993 to 1996		.50
1997 to 2000	Modified Reverse	.50

Note: Fifty cents 2002P to 2009L are issued only in rolls of 25, by the Mint.

Composition Mark

ELIZABETH II, DIADEMED PORTRAIT, NICKEL PLATED STEEL, 1999P - 2003P

Date and Mint Mark	Buying Price
1999P	5.00
2000P	1,500.00
2001P	.50
2002P (1952-)	.50
2003P	.50

ELIZABETH II, IMPERIAL STATE CROWN PORTRAIT, NICKEL PLATED STEEL, 2002P

Date and Mint Mark	Description	Buying Price
1952-2002P	Jubilee Portrait	.50

ELIZABETH II, UNCROWNED PORTRAIT, NICKEL PLATED STEEL, 2004P - 2006P, and 2006 - 2010

Date and Mint Mark	Buying Price
2004P-2006P	.50
2006-2010	.50

SILVER DOLLARS

1935 Obverse

1936 Obverse

1937 to 1947 Obverse

1935 Reverse

1939 Parliament

1949 Newfoundland

Blunt 7

Pointed 7

1947 Maple Leaf

1947 Dot

1952 Water Lines   1952 No Water Lines

GEORGE V 1935 - 1936

Date and Mint Mark	Description	Buying VF Price
1935	Silver Jubilee	14.00
1936	Voyageur	10.00

GEORGE VI 1937 - 1946

Date and Mint Mark	Description	Buying VF Price
1937	Voyageur	10.00
1938	Voyageur	25.00
1939	Royal Visit	8.00
1945	Voyageur	90.00
1946	Voyageur	18.00

GEORGE VI 1947 - 1952

Date and Mint Mark	Description	Buying VF Price
1947	Blunt 7	55.00
1947	Pointed 7	75.00
1947 Dot	Pointed 7	80.00
1947	Maple Leaf	100.00
1948	Dei Gratia	700.00
1949	Newfoundland	8.00
1950	Voyageur	8.00
1950	Arnprior	8.00
1951	Voyageur	8.00
1951	Arnprior	20.00
1952	Water Lines	8.00
1952	Arnprior	10.00
1952	No Water Lines	8.00

IMPORTANT: The silver dollar buying prices are for problem free coins in **Very Fine (VF)** condition. Damaged coins will bring lower prices.

| 1953 Obverse | 1959 Reverse | 1964 Charlottetown |

| 1958 British Columbia | 1965 Reverse | 1967 Centennial |

| 1955 4 Water Lines | 1955 1½ Water Lines | 1957 4 Water Lines | 1957 1½ Water Lines |

ELIZABETH II, LAUREATED PORTRAIT, 1953 - 1960

Date and Mint Mark	Description	Buying VF Price
1953	Voyageur	7.00
1954	Voyageur	7.00
1955	Voyageur	7.00
1955 Arnprior	1½ Waterlines	15.00
1956	Voyageur	7.00
1957	Voyageur	7.00
1957	1½ Waterlines	7.00
1958	British Columbia	7.00
1959	Voyageur	7.00
1960	Voyageur	7.00

ELIZABETH II, TIARA PORTRAIT, 1961 - 1967

Date and Mint Mark	Description	Buying VF Price
1961	Voyageur	7.00
1962	Voyageur	7.00
1963	Voyageur	7.00
1964	Charlottetown	7.00
1965	Voyageur, Medal	7.00
1965	Voyageur, Coinage	1,000.00
1966	Voyageur	7.00
1966 Sm Beads	Voyageur	1,500.00
1967	Centennial, Medal	7.00
1967	Centennial, Coinage	1,000.00

DIE AXIS

The obverse design is considered the primary side of the coin. The die axis is the relationship of the reverse design to the obverse. Consider the obverse die, usually the anvil die in a press, stationary and when installed is the point of reference. The reverse die (moving hammer die) may be turned or set at any of 360 degrees in relation to the set obverse die. If the obverse die is identified by an up-right arrow (↑) then the reverse die may be represented by a second arrow(↑). These arrows form a relationship. Illustrated below are two common die alignments:

Coinage Axis: ↑↓
  Obverse die: ↑
  Reverse die is set 180 degrees opposite: ↓

Medal Axis: ↑↑
  Obverse die: ↑
  Reverse die is set in the matching direction: ↑

NICKEL DOLLARS

Common Obverse

Voyageur Reverse

1968 Island

1968 No Island

Manitoba

British Columbia

Prince Edward Island

Winnipeg

Constitution

Jacques Cartier

ELIZABETH II, TIARA PORTRAIT, 1968 - 1973

Date and Mint Mark	Description	Buying Price
1968	Voyageur	1.00
1968	Small Island	4.00
1968	No Island	2.00
1969	Voyageur	1.00
1970	Manitoba	1.00
1971	British Columbia	1.00
1972	Voyageur	1.00
1973	P.E.I.	1.00

ELIZABETH II, TIARA PORTRAIT, 1974 - 1986

Date and Mint Mark	Description	Buying Price
1974	Winnipeg	1.00
1975 to 1981	Voyageur	1.00
1982	Constitution, Medal	1.00
1982	Consitution, Coinage	500.00
1983	Voyageur	1.00
1984	Jacques Cartier	1.00
1985	Voyageur	1.00
1986	Voyageur	1.00

NICKEL BRONZE DOLLARS

ELIZABETH II, TIARA PORTRAIT, 1987 - 1989

Date and Mint Mark	Description	Buying Price
1987	Loon, Unc	1.00
1987	Loon, Proof	4.00
1988	Loon	1.00
1989	Loon	1.00

ELIZABETH II, DIADEMED PORTRAIT, 1992 - 1993

Date and Mint Mark	Description	Buying Price
1867-1992	Double Date	1.00
1993	Loon	1.00

ELIZABETH II, DIADEMED PORTRAIT, 1994

Date and Mint Mark	Description	Buying Price
1994	Remembrance, Unc	1.00
1994	Remembrance, Proof	4.00
1994	Loon	1.00

ELIZABETH II, DIADEMED PORTRAIT, 1990 - 1991

Date and Mint Mark	Description	Buying Price
1990 to 1991	Loon	1.00

CANADA 125 ANNIVERSARY

ELIZABETH II, DIADEMED PORTRAIT, 1992

Date and Mint Mark	Description	Buying Price
1992	Unc	1.00

ELIZABETH II, DIADEMED PORTRAIT, 1995

Date and Mint Mark	Description	Buying Price
1995	Peacekeeping, Unc	1.00
1995	Peacekeeping, Proof	4.00

IMPORTANT: Do not clean your coins. Coins should be handled carefully. Only experts should consider cleaning. If you are not an expert, the results can be disastrous.

Note: Proof issues of 1987, 1992, 1994 and 1995 were issued by the Numismatic Deptartment of the Royal Canadian Mint.

ELIZABETH II, DIADEMED PORTRAIT, 1995 - 1996

Date and Mint Mark	Description	Buying Price
1995	Loon	1.00
1996	Loon	1.00
1997 to 2001	Not Issued	

ELIZABETH II, DIADEMED PORTRAIT, 2002

Date and Mint Mark	Description	Buying Price
1952-2002	Jubilee	1.00

2004 Lucky Loonie   2005 Terry Fox

2006 Loon Settling

ELIZABETH II, UNCROWNED PORTRAIT, 2003 - 2006

Date and Mint Mark	Description	Buying Price
2003	Loon	1.00
2004	Loon	1.00
2004	Loon and Olympic Flames	1.00
2005	Loon	1.00
2005	Terry Fox	1.00
2006	Loon	1.00
2006	Loon Settling	1.00

Royal Canadian Mint Logo

2008 Loon Dance   2009 Montreal Canadiens

Vanvcouver 2010
Winter Olympic Games

ELIZABETH II, UNCROWNED PORTRAIT, LOGO, 2006 - 2010

Date and Mint Mark	Description	Buying Price
2006	Loon	1.00
2007	Loon	1.00
2008	Loon	1.00
2008	Loon Dance	1.00
2009	Loon	1.00
2009	Montreal Canadiens	1.00
2010	Vancouver 2010 Olympics	1.00

TWO DOLLAR COINS

ELIZABETH II, DIADEMED PORTRAIT 1996 - 1998

Date and Mint Mark	Description	Buying Price
1996	Polar Bear	2.00
1997	Polar Bear	2.00
1998	Polar Bear	2.00

ELIZABETH II, DIADEMED PORTRAIT, 2001 - 2003

Date and Mint Mark	Description	Buying Price
2001	Polar Bear	2.00
1952-2002	Double Date	2.00
2003	Polar Bear	2.00

ELIZABETH II, DIADEMED PORTRAIT, 1999

Date and Mint Mark	Description	Buying Price
1999	Nunavut	2.00

ELIZABETH II, UNCROWNED PORTRAIT, 2003 - 2006

Date and Mint Mark	Description	Buying Price
2003	Polar Bear	2.00
2004	Polar Bear	2.00
2005	Polar Bear	2.00
2006	Polar Bear	2.00

ELIZABETH II, DIADEMED PORTRAIT, 2000

Date and Mint Mark	Description	Buying Price
2000	Polar Bears	2.00

1996-2006 10th Anniversary

Royal
Canadian
Mint
Logo

1996-2006 10th Anniversary "Churchill"

ELIZABETH II, UNCROWNED PORTRAIT, 2006

Date and Mint Mark	Description	Buying Price
2006	10th Anniv.	2.00
2006	Churchill	2.00

2009 400th Anniversary Quebec City

ELIZABETH II, UNCROWNED PORTRAIT, LOGO, 2006 - 2010

Date and Mint Mark	Description	Buying Price
2006	Polar Bear	2.00
2007	Polar Bear	2.00
2008	Polar Bear	2.00
2009	Polar Bear	2.00
2009	400th Anniv. Quebec City	2.00
2010	Polar Bear	2.00

CIRCULATING GOLD COINS

SOVEREIGNS

EDWARD VII 1908 - 1910

Date and Mint Mark	Buying VF Price
1908C	1,200.00
1909C	300.00
1910C	300.00

GEORGE V 1911 - 1919

Date and Mint Mark	Buying VF Price
1911C	295.00
1913C	350.00
1914C	295.00
1916C	10,000.00
1917C	295.00
1918C	295.00
1919C	295.00

FIVE DOLLARS

GEORGE V 1912 - 1914

Date and Mint Mark	Buying VF Price
1912	300.00
1913	300.00
1914	350.00

TEN DOLLARS

GEORGE V 1912 - 1914

Date and Mint Mark	Buying VF Price
1912	600.00
1913	600.00
1914	650.00

IMPORTANT: Do not clean your coins. Coins should be handled carefully. Only experts should consider cleaning. If you are not an expert, the results can be disastrous.

COLLECTOR COINS

The numismatic department of the Royal Canadian Mint issued specially struck and packaged coins starting in 1954. The coins were issued for collectors and as a result are of high quality. The dealer buying prices listed below are for single coins and sets in their original packaging and condition. Coins or sets which have been mishandled or damaged are discounted from the prices listed. Beginning in 1971 the numismatic department of the Royal Canadian Mint issued silver dollars for collectors in two conditions, proof and uncirculated. Proof condition dollars were issued in black leatherette boxes while uncirculated dollars were issued in a clear plastic container.

ONE CENT

Date	Description	Buying Price
2003	Selectively gold plated	15.00

SILVER THREE CENTS

Date	Description	Buying Price
2001	3 Cent Beaver	5.00

SILVER FIVE CENTS

2000-2002
Common Obv.

Les Voltigeurs
de Québec

Royal Military
College of Canada

85th Anniv. Battle
for Vimy Ridge

Date	Description	Buying Price
2000	Les Voltigeurs de Québec	3.00
2001	Royal Military College, Canada	3.00
2002	85th Anniversary, Vimy Ridge	10.00

60th Anniversary D-Day 1944-2004

60th Anniversary VE-Day 1945-2005

1945-2005
Selectively
gold platead

Date	Description	Buying Price
2004	60th Anniv. D-Day	18.00
005	60th Anniv. VE-Day	6.00
2006	1945-2005 Gold plated	12.00

SILVER TEN CENTS

Caboto

Date	Description	Buying Price
1997	Caboto	5.00

100th Anniv. Credit Unions in N.A. 2000

Year of the Volunteers, 2001

Canadian Open Golf, 2004

Date	Description	Buying Price
2000	100th Anniv. Credit Unions	1.00
2001	Int'l Year of Volunteers	1.00
2004	Canadian Open Golf	4.00

TWENTY-FIVE CENTS
125TH ANNIVERSARY 1867-1992

For the complete 12-coin set of the 1867-1992, 125th Anniversary see page 24. The set was minted in both nickel and silver

January - New Brunswick

Date	Description	No. of Coins	Buying Price
1992	125th Anniversary silver proof set	13	35.00
1992	Single silver coin	1	2.00
1992	125 Anniversary nickel souvenier set	13	5.00

TWENTY-FIVE CENTS
1999 and 2000 MILLENNIUM

For the complete 24-coin set of the 1999-2000 millennium celebration see pages 26 and 27. The coins were issued in both nickel and silver.

January 1999

1999 Millennium Medallion

September 1999 Mule
Obverse has no denomination

November 1999 Mule
Obverse has no denomination

Date	Description	Buying Price
1999	12 coin set and 1999 medallion	2.00
1999	September, no denomination	25.00
1999	November, no denomination	25.00
1999	Medallion	1.00
1999	12 coin silver set	35.00
1999	Single silver coin	3.00

TWENTY-FIVE CENTS

2000 MILLENNIUM

January 2000, for complete set see pages 26-27.

2000 Millennium Medallion

2000 Mule
Coin Obverse with Medallion Obverse

Date	Description	Buying Price
2000	12-coin, medallion	4.00
2000	Medallion	1.00
2000	Coin; medallion mule	200.00
2000	12-coin silver set	35.00
2000	Single silver coin	2.00

CANADA'S FIRST COLOURISED COIN

Obv. 2000-2003

Date	Description	Buying Price
2000	January	4.00

CANADA DAY SERIES

Canada Day 2000   Canada Day 2001

Canada Day 2002   Canada Day 2003

Obv. 2004-2008   Canada Day, 2004

Moose 2004   Canada Day 2005

Canada Day 2006   Canada Day 2007

Canada Day 2008   Canada Day 2009

CANADA DAY SERIES (cont.)

Date	Description	Buying Price
2000	Canada Day 2000	25.00
2001P	Canada Day 2001	3.00
2002P	Canada Day 2002	3.00
2003P	Canada Day 2003	5.00
2004P	Canada Day 2004	4.00
2004P	Moose 2004	5.00
2005P	Canada Day 2005	4.00
2006P	Canada Day 2006	4.00
2007	Canada Day 2007	4.00
2008	Canada Day 2008	4.00
2009	Canada Day 2009	4.00

CHRISTMAS DAY

2004 Santa Claus

2005 Christmas Stocking / 2006 Santa in Sleigh

2007 Christmas Tree / 2008 Santa

Date	Description	Buying Price
2004	Santa Claus	10.00
2005	Christmas Stocking	5.00
2006	Santa in Sleigh	4.00
2007	Christmas Tree	4.00
2008	Santa	4.00

2004 Poppy

2005 Poppy / 2006 Liberation

Date	Description	Buying Price
2004	Poppy, Silver	10.00
2005P	Poppy*	4.00
2006P	Liberation, Silver	20.00

QUEBEC WINTER CARNIVAL

Date	Description	Buying Price
2006P	Quebec Winter Carnival	4.00

BREAST CANCER AWARENESS

Date	Description	Buying Price
2006P	Breast Cancer Awareness*	4.00

Note: * These coins were encased in a plastic bookmark.

HOCKEY SERIES (Gift and Holiday Sets)

2005-2006 HOCKEY SEASON

Common Obv.

Montreal Canadiens

Ottawa Senators

Toronto Maple Leafs

2006-2007 HOCKEY SEASON

Common Obv.

Calgary Flames

Edmonton Oilers

Montreal Canadiens

Ottawa Senators

Toronto Maple Leafs

Vancouver Canucks

Date	Description	Buying Price
2006P	Montreal Canadiens	5.00
2006P	Ottawa Senators	5.00
2006P	Toronto Maple Leafs	5.00
2007L	Calgary Flames	5.00
2007L	Edmonton Oilers	5.00
2007L	Montreal Canadiens	5.00
2007L	Ottawa Senators	5.00
2007L	Toronto Maple Leafs	5.00
2007L	Vancouver Canucks	5.00

QUEEN ELIZABETH II COMMEMORATIVES

2006 80th Birthday of Queen
Elizabeth II

2007 60th Wedding Anniversary
Queen Elizabeth II

Date	Description	Buying Price
2006	80th Birthday Queen Elizabeth II	5.00
2007	60th Wedding Anniversary	5.00

COLOURISED OCCASIONS SERIES (Gift and Holiday Sets)

OCCASIONS – 2007

Common Obv.

Baby / Rattle

Birthday / Balloons

Congratulations / Fireworks

Oh! Canada / Maple Leaf

Wedding / Bouquet

OCCASIONS – 2008

Common Obv.

Baby / Teddy Bear

Birthday / Party Hat

Congratulations / Trophy

Oh! Canada / Flag

Wedding / Cake

OCCASIONS - 2009

Baby / Teddy Bear, Moon

Oh! Canada / Maple Leaves

Date	Description	Buying Price
2007	Baby / Rattle	5.00
2007	Birthday / Balloons	5.00
2007	Congratulations / Fireworks	5.00
2007	Oh! Canada / Maple Leaf	5.00
2007	Wedding / Bouquet	5.00
2008	Baby / Teddy Bear	5.00

Date	Description	Buying Price
2008	Birthday / Party Hat	5.00
2008	Congratulations / Trophy	5.00
2008	Oh! Canada / Flag	5.00
2008	Wedding / Cake	5.00
2009	Baby / Teddy Bear, Moon	5.00
2009	Oh! Canada / Maple Leaves	5.00

BIRD SERIES

Ruby-Throated Hummingbird

Red-Breasted Nuthatch

Downy Woodpecker

Cardinal

Date	Description	Buying Price
2007	Ruby-Throated Hummingbird	5.00
2007	Red-Breasted Nuthatch	5.00
2008	Downy Woodpecker	5.00
2009	Cardinal	5.00

ANNE OF GREEN GABLES

Date	Description	Buying Price
2008	Anne of Green Gables	5.00

CARDS WITH COINS

Birthday · Congratulations

Thank You · Wedding

Date	Description	Buying Price
2009	Birthday	2.50
2009	Congratulations	2.50
2009	Thank You	2.50
2009	Wedding	2.50

Note: Prices are for coins in their original packaging.

PROOF SILVER FIFTY CENTS
WILD LIFE SERIES

| Atlantic Puffin | Whooping Crane | Gray Jays | White Tailed Ptarmigans |

Date	Description	Buying Price	Date	Description	Buying Price
1995	Atlantic Puffins	6.00	1995	Gray Jays	6.00
1995	Whooping Crane	6.00	1995	White Tailed Ptarmigans	6.00

| Moose Calf | Wood Ducklings | Cougar Kittens | Black Bear Cubs |

Date	Description	Buying Price	Date	Description	Buying Price
1996	Moose Calf	6.00	1996	Cougar Kittens	6.00
1996	Wood Ducklings	6.00	1996	Black Bear Cubs	6.00

| Newfoundland | Nova Scotia Duck Tolling Retriever | Labrador Retriever | Canadian Eskimo Dog |

Date	Description	Buying Price	Date	Description	Buying Price
1997	Newfoundland	6.00	1997	Labrador Retriever	6.00
1997	Nova Scotia Duck Tolling Retriever	6.00	1997	Canadian Eskimo Dog	6.00

PROOF SILVER FIFTY CENTS
WILD LIFE SERIES

Killer Whale

Humpback Whale

Beluga Whale

Blue Whale

Date	Description	Buying Price
1998	Killer Whale	6.00
1998	Humpback Whale	6.00

Date	Description	Buying Price
1998	Beluga Whale	6.00
1998	Blue Whale	6.00

Tonkinese

Lynx

Cymric

Cougar

Date	Description	Buying Price
1999	Tonkinese	10.00
1999	Lynx	10.00

Date	Description	Buying Price
1999	Cymric	10.00
1999	Cougar	10.00

Bald Eagle

Osprey

Great Horned Owl

Red-Tailed Hawk

Date	Description	Buying Price
2000	Bald Eagle	6.00
2000	Osprey	6.00

Date	Description	Buying Price
2000	Great Horned Owl	6.00
2000	Red-Tailed Hawk	6.00

PROOF SILVER FIFTY CENTS
SPORTS SERIES

Skating

Skiing

Soccer

Auto Racing

Date	Description	Buying Price
1998	Skating	6.00
1998	Skiing	6.00

Date	Description	Buying Price
1998	Soccer	6.00
1998	Auto Racing	6.00

Golf

Yacht Race

Football

Basketball

Date	Description	Buying Price
1999	Golf	7.00
1999	Yacht Race	6.00

Date	Description	Buying Price
1999	Football	6.00
1999	Basketball	6.00

Hockey

Curling

Steeplechase

Bowling

Date	Description	Buying Price
2000	Hockey	6.00
2000	Curling	6.00

Date	Description	Buying Price
2000	Steeplechase	6.00
2000	Bowling	6.00

PROOF SILVER FIFTY CENTS
CANADIAN FESTIVALS SERIES

Quebec Winter
Carnival (Quebec)

Toonik Tyme
(Nunavut)

Newfoundland and
Labrador Folk Festival
(Newfoundland)

Festival of Fathers
(Prince Edward Island)

Annapolis Valley Blossom
Festival
(Nova Scotia)

Stratford Festival of
Canada (Ontario)

Folklorama
(Manitoba)

Calgary Stampede
(Alberta)

Squamish Days
Logger Sports
(British Columbia)

Yukon Festival
(Yukon)

Back to Batoche
(Saskatchewan)

Great Northern
Arts Festival
(Northwest Territories)

Festival Acadien
de Caraquet
(New Brunswick)

Date	Description	Price	Date	Description	Price
2001	Québec	6.00	2002	Alberta	6.00
2001	Nunavut	6.00	2002	British Columbia	6.00
2001	Newfoundland	6.00	2003	Yukon	6.00
2001	Prince Edward Island	6.00	2003	Saskatchewan	6.00
2002	Nova Scotia	6.00	2003	Northwest Territories	6.00
2002	Ontario	6.00	2003	New Brunswick	6.00
2002	Manitoba	6.00	2001-03	Set Can. Festivals (13 coins)	80.00

PROOF SILVER FIFTY CENTS
CANADIAN FOLKLORE AND LEGENDS SERIES

The Sled

The Maiden's Cave

Les Petits Sauteux

The Pig That Wouldn't

Shoemaker in Heaven

Le Vaisseau Fantome

Date	Description	Price	Date	Description	Price
2001	The Sled	6.00	2002	The Pig That Wouldn't	6.00
2001	The Maiden's Cave	6.00	2002	Shoemaker in Heaven	6.00
2001	Les Petits Sauteux	6.00	2002	Le Vaisseau Fantome	6.00

FLOWER SERIES

Golden Tulip

Golden Daffodil

Golden Lily

Golden Rose

Golden Daisy

Golden Forget Me Not

Date	Description	Price	Date	Description	Price
2002	Golden Tulip	30.00	2005	Golden Rose	10.00
2003	Golden Daffodil	10.00	2006	Golden Daisy	10.00
2004	Golden Lily	10.00	2007	Golden Forget Me Not	10.00

PROOF SILVER FIFTY CENTS
COAT OF ARMS OF CANADA

| Kruger-Gray 1953 | Shingles 1954-1958 | Shingles 1959-1996 | Bursey-Sabourin 1997-2010 |

Date	Description	Buying Price	Date	Description	Buying Price
2004	Kruger-Gray, 1953	8.00	2004	Shingles 1959-1996	8.00
2004	Shingles, 1954-1958	8.00	2004	Bursey-Sabourin, 1997-2010	8.00

CANADIAN BUTTERFLY COLLECTION

| Canadian Tiger Swallowtail | Canadian Clouded Sulpher | Monarch |

| Spangled Fritillary | Short-tailed Swallowtail | Silvery Blue |

Date	Description	Buying Price	Date	Description	Buying Price
2003	Canadian Tiger Swallowtail	15.00	2005	Spangled Fritillary	15.00
2004	Canadian Clouded Sulpher	15.00	2006	Short-tailed Swallowtail	15.00
2005	Monarch	15.00	2007	Silvery Blue	15.00

QUEST FOR PEACE AND FREEDOM DURING SECOND WORLD WAR

Battle of Britain

Liberation of Netherlands

Conquest of Sicily

Battle of the Scheldt

Raid on Dieppe

Battle of the Atlantic

Date	Description	Buying Price	Date	Description	Buying Price
2005	Battle of Britain	8.00	2005	Battle of the Scheldt	8.00
2005	Liberation of Netherlands	8.00	2005	Raid on Dieppe	8.00
2005	Conquest of Sicily	8.00	2005	Battle of the Atlantic	8.00

HOCKEY LEGENDS

Jean Beliveau

Guy Lafleur

Jacques Plante

Maurice Richard

Johnny Bower

Tim Horton

Darryl Sittler

Dave Keon

Date	Description	Buying Price	Date	Description	Buying Price
2005	Jean Beliveau	7.00	2005	Johnny Bower	7.00
2005	Guy Lafleur	7.00	2005	Tim Horton	7.00
2005	Jacques Plante	7.00	2005	Darryl Sittler	7.00
2005	Maurice Richard	7.00	2005	Dave Keon	7.00

SILVER PROOF-LIKE DOLLARS

Single dollars, in either cellophane or pliofilm packaging, were issued by the Royal Canadian Mint for collectors. Illustrations of these dollars can be found on page 35.

Date	Description	Buying Price	Date	Description	Buying Price
1954	Voyageur	250.00	1959	Voyageur	20.00
1955	Voyageur	150.00	1960	Voyageur	15.00
1955	Arnprior	225.00	1961	Voyageur	9.00
1956	Voyageur	100.00	1962	Voyageur	9.00
1957	Voyageur	60.00	1963	Voyageur	9.00
1958	British Columbia	40.00	1964	Charlottetown	9.00

CASED NICKEL DOLLARS

1970 Manitoba

1971 British Columbia

1973 Prince Edward Island

1974 Winnipeg

1982 Constitution

1984 Jacques Cartier

Date	Description	Buying Price	Date	Description	Buying Price
1970	Manitoba	1.25	1975	Voyageur	1.25
1971	British Columbia	1.25	1976	Voyageur	1.25
1972	Voyageur	1.25	1982	Constitution	2.00
1973	Prince Edward Island	1.25	1984	Jacques Cartier	2.00
1974	Winnipeg	1.25			

Note: Coins must be as issued in clam style Mint cases.

CASED SILVER DOLLARS

Common Obverse

1971 British Columbia

1973 R.C.M.P.

1974 Winnipeg Centennial

1975 Calgary

1976 Library of Parliament

1977 Silver Jubilee

1978 Commonwealth Games

1979 Griffon Tricentennial

Date	Description	Buying Price	Date	Description	Buying Price
1971	British Columbia Centennial	5.00	1976	Library of Parliament	5.00
1972	Voyageur	5.00	1977	Silver Jubilee	5.00
1973	R.C.M.P.	5.00	1978	Commonwealth Games	5.00
1974	Winnipeg Centennial	5.00	1979	Griffon Tricentennial	5.00
1975	Calgary Stampede	5.00			

CASED SILVER DOLLARS

1980 Arctic Territories

1981 Trans-Canada Railway

1982 Regina Centennial

1983 World University Games

1984 Toronto Sesquicentennial

1985 National Parks Centannial

1986 Vancouver Centennial

1987 John Davis Strait

1988 Saint-Maurice Ironworks

Date	Description	Buying Price
1980	Arctic Territories Centennial	6.00
1981	Trans-Canada Railway (PR)	6.00
1981	Trans-Canada Railway (UNC)	5.00
1982	Regina Centennial (PR)	5.00
1982	Regina Centennial (UNC)	5.00
1983	World University Games (PR)	5.00
1983	World University Games (UNC)	5.00
1984	Toronto Sesquicentennial (PR)	5.00
1984	Toronto Sesquicentennial (UNC)	5.00

Date	Description	Buying Price
1985	National Parks Centennial (PR)	5.00
1985	National Parks Centennial (UNC)	5.00
1986	Vancouver Centennial (PR)	5.00
1986	Vancouver Centennial (UNC)	5.00
1987	Davis Strait (PR)	5.00
1987	Davis Strait (UNC)	5.00
1988	Sainte-Maurice Ironworks(PR)	6.00
1988	Sainte-Maurice Ironworks (UNC)	5.00

CASED SILVER DOLLARS

1989 MacKenzie River

Common Obverse 1990 - 2003

1990 Henry Kelsey Tricentennial

1991 Frontenac

1992 Kingston Stagecoach

1993 Stanley Cup

1994 R.C.M.P. Northern
Dog Team Patrol

1995 325th Anniv. Founding
of Hudson's Bay Co.

1996 200th Anniversary
John McIntosh

Date	Description	Buying Price	Date	Description	Buying Price
1989	MacKenzie River (PR)	7.00	1993	Stanley Cup (PR)	11.00
1989	MacKenzie River (UNC)	5.00	1993	Stanley Cup (UNC)	10.00
1990	Henry Kelsey (PR)	9.00	1994	R.C.M.P. (PR)	12.00
1990	Henry Kelsey (UNC)	5.00	1994	R.C.M.P. (UNC)	10.00
1991	Frontenac (PR)	10.00	1995	Hudson's Bay (PR)	15.00
1991	Frontenac (UNC)	5.00	1995	Hudson's Bay (UNC)	10.00
1992	Kingston Stagecoach (PR)	11.00	1996	McIntosh (PR)	15.00
1992	Kingston Stagecoach (UNC)	10.00	1996	McIntosh (UNC)	10.00

CASED SILVER DOLLARS

1997 Canada/Russia Hockey

1997 Flying Loon

1998 125th Anniversary RCMP

1999 225th Anniv. Juan Perez

1999 Int'l Year Older Persons

2000 Voyage of Discovery

2001 50th Anniversary
National Ballet of Canada

2001 90th Anniversary
Canada's 1911 Silver Dollar

2002 50th Anniv. Elizabeth II's
Accession to the Throne

Date	Description	Buying Price	Date	Description	Buying Price
1997	Hockey (PR)	15.00	2000	Voyage of Discovery (PR)	15.00
1997	Hockey (UNC)	10.00	2000	Voyage of Discovery (UNC)	10.00
1997	Flying Loon (PR)	50.00	2001	National Ballet of Canada (PR)	10.00
1998	RCMP (PR)	12.00	2001	National Ballet of Canada (UNC)	10.00
1998	RCMP (UNC)	10.00	2001	90th Anniv. 1911 Silver Dollar (PR)	20.00
1999	Perez (PR)	15.00	2002	50th Anniv. Accession (PR)	14.00
1999	Perez (UNC)	10.00	2002	50th Anniv. Accession (UNC)	10.00
1999	Older Persons (PR)	20.00			

Note: **(PR)** Proof condition one dollar silver coins are issued in a black leatherette case.
(UNC) UNC condition one dollar silver coins are issued in a clear plastic case.

CASED SILVER DOLLARS

2002 Queen Mother

2003 Cobalt

Common Obv. 2003 to 2006

2003 50th Anniv. Coronation

2004 First French Settlement

2004 The Poppy

2005 40th Anniv. Canadian Flag

2006 150th Anniv. Victoria Cross

2007 Medal of Bravery

Date	Description	Buying Price
2002	Queen Mother (PR)	100.00
2003	Cobalt (PR)	11.00
2003	Cobalt (Unc)	10.00
2003	Coronation (PR)	15.00
2004	First French Settlement (PR)	15.00
2004	First French Settlement (Unc)	10.00
2004	First French Settle. Privy Mark	25.00
2004	Lucky Loon (PR)	25.00
2004	Poppy (PR)	15.00

Date	Description	Buying Price
2005	40th Anniv. Can. Flag (PR)	15.00
2005	40th Anniv. Can. Flag (Unc)	10.00
2005	40th Anniv. Can. Flag (En.)	100.00
2006	Victoria Cross (PR)	15.00
2006	Victoria Cross (Unc)	10.00
2006	Victoria Cross (Gold Plated)	30.00
2006	Medal of Bravery (PR)	20.00
2006	Medal of Bravery (En.)	75.00

Note: (PR) Proof
(Unc) Uncirculated
(En.) Enamelled

CASED SILVER DOLLARS

2007 Obverse

2007 Thayendanegna

2007 Celebration of the Arts

2008 Quebec City

2008 RCM 100th Anniv.

2008 Armistice

2009 Flight in Canada

2010 Navy, 100th Anniversary

Date	Description	Buying Price	Date	Description	Buying Price
2007	Thayendanegea (PR)	15.00	2008	Armistice (PR)	30.00
2007	Thayendanegea (Unc)	11.00	2009	Flight in Canada (PR)	15.00
2007	Celebration of the Arts (PR)	25.00	2009	Flight in Canada (Unc)	11.00
2008	Quebec City (PR)	15.00	2010	Navy, 100th Anniv. (PR)	15.00
2008	Quebec City (Unc)	11.00	2010	Navy, 100th Anniv (Unc)	11.00
2008	RCM 100th Anniv.	30.00			

SILVER LOON DOLLARS

Common Obv. 2004-2006	2004 Olympic Loon	2006 Loon Settling	2006 Lullabies Loonie
2006 Obverse with Mint Logo	2006 Snowflake	2007 Loon	2008 Loon
2008 Obverse	2008 Loon Dance	2010 Obverse	2010 Anticipating the Games

Date	Description	Buying Price		Date	Description	Buying Price
2004	Olympic Loon (PR)	20.00		2007	Loon	15.00
2006	Loon Settling (PR)	15.00		2008	Loon	15.00
2006	Lullabies Loonie (PR)	15.00		2008	Loon Dance	15.00
2006	Snowflake	15.00		2010	Anticipating the Games	15.00

Note: The silver loon dollars were not issued for circulation. They were sold by the Mint, individually or in sets.

BRONZE DOLLARS

| 1992 125th Anniv. | 1994 Remembrance | 1995 Peacekeeping | 1997 Loon Rising |

| 2002 Family of Loons | 2002 Centre Ice | 2004 Canada Goose | 2004 Elusive Loon |

| 2005 Tufted Puffin | 2006 Snowy Owl | 2007 Common Obv. | 2007 Trumpeter Swan |

| 2008 Loon Dance | 2008 Common Eider | 2009 Great Blue Heron. | Vanvcouver 2010 |

Date	Description	Buying Price	Date	Description	Buying Price
1992	125th Anniv. of Canada	3.00	2005	Tufted Puffin	20.00
1994	Remembrance	3.00	2006	Snowy Owl	20.00
1995	Peacekeeping	3.00	2007	Trumpeter Swan	10.00
1997	Loon Rising	20.00	2008	Loon Dance	10.00
2002	Family of Loons	12.00	2008	Common Eider	10.00
2002	Centre Ice	12.00	2009	Great Blue Heron	10.00
2004	Canada Goose	20.00	2010	Vancouver 2010 Olympics	10.00
2005	Elusive Loon	20.00			

Note: The bronze collector dollars of 1992-2010 were issued in specimen or proof sets.

1 DOLLAR

2007-2008 HOCKEY SEASON (Gift Sets)

Calgary Flames

Edmonton Oilers

Montreal Canadiens

Ottawa Senators

Toronto Maple Leafs

Vancouver Canucks

Date	Description	Buying Price	Date	Description	Buying Price
2008	Calgary Flames	5.00	2008	Ottawa Sentaors	5.00
2008	Edmonton Oilers	5.00	2008	Toronto Maple Leafs	5.00
2008	Montreal Canadiens	5.00	2008	Vancouver Canucks	5.00

2007-2008 HOCKEY SEASON AND VANCOUVER 2010 OLYMPIC WINTER GAMES (Pucks)

Calgary Flames

Edmonton Oilers

Montreal Canadiens

Ottawa Senatoes

Toronto Maple Leafs

Vancouver Canucks

Vanvcouver 2010

Date	Description	Buying Price	Date	Description	Buying Price
2008	Calgary Flames	5.00	2008	Toronto Maple Leafs	5.00
2008	Edmonton Oilers	5.00	2008	Vancouver Canucks	5.00
2008	Montreal Canadiens	5.00	2008	Vancouver 2010 Lucky Loonie	5.00
2008	Ottawa Senators	5.00			

2 DOLLAR COINS

1996 Polar Bear   2000 Polar Bears

ELIZABETH II 1996

Date	Description	Buying Price
1996	Proof	3.00
1996	Piedfort	30.00
1996	Gold	150.00

ELIZABETH II 2000

Date	Description	Buying Price
2000	Proof	10.00
2000	Silver	8.00
2000	Gold	150.00

1999 Nunavut - Ring   2004 Polar Bear, Silver

ELIZABETH II 2004

Date	Description	Buying Price
2004	Polar Bear, Silver	15.00

1999 Nunavut - No Ring   2006 Gold

ELIZABETH II 1999

Date	Description	Buying Price
1999	Silver	8.00
1999	Gold	150.00
1999	Mule, No Ring	100.00

ELIZABETH II 2006

Date	Description	Buying Price
2006	10th Anniv. Gold Two Dollar	150.00

3 DOLLAR COIN

THE BEAVER

Date	Description	Buying Price
2006	The Beaver	75.00

4 DOLLAR COINS

DINOSAUR COLLECTION

| Common Obverse | 2007 Parasaurolophus | 2008 Triceratops | 2009 Tyrannosaurus Rex |

Date	Description	Buying Price
2007	Parasaurolophus	75.00
2008	Triceratops	40.00
2009	Tyrannosaurus Rex	20.00

5 DOLLAR COIN

VIKING SETTLEMENT

| Canada $5 | Norway 20 Kroner |

Date	Description	Buying Price
1999	Viking Settlement (copper)	15.00

5 DOLLAR SILVER COINS

50TH ANNIVERSARY OF BETHUNE'S ARRIVAL IN CHINA

Canada $5

China

100TH ANNIVERSARY OF MARCONI'S FIRST MESSAGE ACROSS THE ATLANTIC

Canada $5

British £2

2006 WORLD CUP OF SOCCER, GERMANY

Date	Description	Buying Price
1998	Bethune, 2 coin set	20.00
2001	Marconi, 2 coin set	18.00

Date	Description	Buying Price
2003	World Cup	12.00

5 DOLLAR SILVER COINS

Common obv. (except
for date) 2004-2005

2004 100th Anniversary
Canadian Open Championship

2004 Majestic Moose

2005 60th Anniversary of the end
of the Second World War

Common obv. 2005-2006

2005 Alberta Centennial

2005 Saskatchewan Centennial

Obverse 2006

2006 Breast Cancer

Date	Description	Buying Price	Date	Description	Buying Price
2004	100th Anniv. Canadian Open Golf	10.00	2005	Alberta Centennial	18.00
2004	Majestic Moose	75.00	2005	Saskatchewan Centennial	18.00
2005	60th Anniv. WWII.	15.00	2006	Breast Cancer	20.00

5 DOLLAR SILVER COINS

Common obv. 2005-2006

2005 White-tailed Deer and Fawn

2005 Atlantic Walrus and Calf

2006 Peregrine Falcon and Nestlings

2006 Sable Island Horse and Foal

2006 Snowbirds

Date	Description	Buying Price	Date	Description	Buying Price
2005	White-tailed Deer and Fawn	18.00	2006	Sable Island Horse and Foal	18.00
2005	Atlantic Walrus and Calf	18.00	2006	Snowbirds	20.00
2006	Peregrine Falcon and Nestlings	18.00			

5 AND 10 DOLLAR SILVER COINS
MONTREAL 1976 OLYMPIC GAMES

For the Summer Olympic Games of 1976, held in Montreal, seven series of silver coins were minted. There were four different coins in each series. Two $5.00 and two $10.00 coins, struck in sterling silver. The $5.00 coins weigh 24.3 grams and the $10.00 coins weigh 48.6 grams. The coins were available, encapsulated in plastic, as single coins, and in custom, prestige and proof four-coin sets. Each set of four coins, with a face value of $30.00, contains 4.28 oz. of fine silver. The purchase price of these sets is linked to the market price of silver, even if the intrinsic value falls below the face value. Large quantities of these coins were issued, and they are not redeemable by the government or the banks.

SERIES I

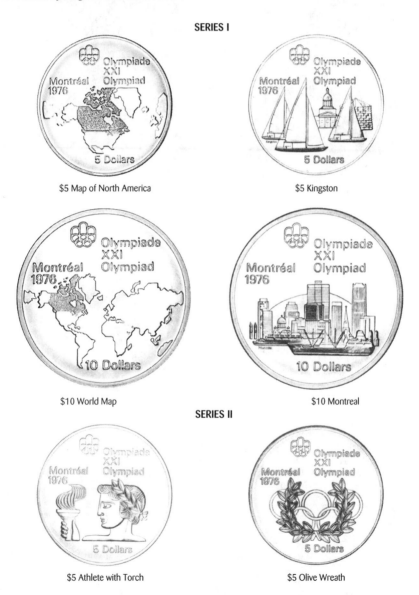

$5 Map of North America

$5 Kingston

$10 World Map

$10 Montreal

SERIES II

$5 Athlete with Torch

$5 Olive Wreath

72

5 AND 10 DOLLAR SILVER COINS

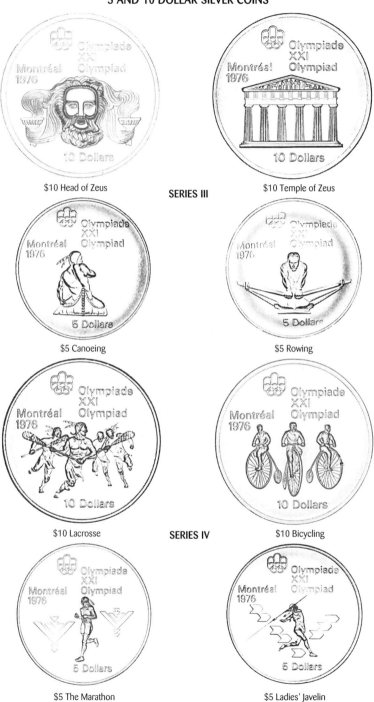

$10 Head of Zeus

SERIES III

$10 Temple of Zeus

$5 Canoeing

$5 Rowing

$10 Lacrosse

SERIES IV

$10 Bicycling

$5 The Marathon

$5 Ladies' Javelin

5 AND 10 DOLLAR SILVER COINS

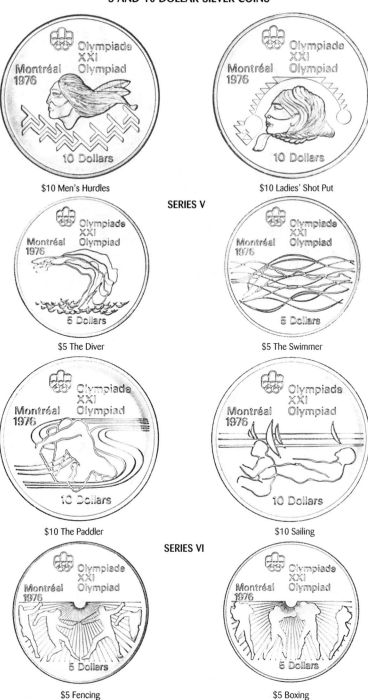

$10 Men's Hurdles

$10 Ladies' Shot Put

SERIES V

$5 The Diver

$5 The Swimmer

$10 The Paddler

$10 Sailing

SERIES VI

$5 Fencing

$5 Boxing

5 AND 10 DOLLAR SILVER COINS

$10 Field Hockey

$10 Football

SERIES VII

$5 Olympic Flame

$5 Oylmpic Village

$10 Olympic Stadium

$10 Olympic Velodrome

Date	Series	$5 Coin	$10 Coin	Custom Set	Prestige Set	Proof Set
1973	1	9.00	18.00	54.00	54.00	54.00
1974	Mule	–	150.00	–	–	–
1974	2	9.00	18.00	54.00	54.00	54.00
1974	3	9.00	18.00	54.00	54.00	54.00
1975	4	9.00	18.00	54.00	54.00	54.00
1975	5	9.00	18.00	54.00	54.00	54.00
1976	6	9.00	18.00	54.00	54.00	54.00
1976	7	9.00	18.00	54.00	54.00	54.00

Note: A set equals 2 x $5.00 coins and 2 x $10.00 coins of the same year.

8 DOLLAR SILVER COINS

2004 Great Grizzly

2005 Railway Bridge

2005 Chinese Memorial

2007 Trade in Ancient China Obv.

2007 Trade in Ancient China Rev.

2007 Maple of Long Life

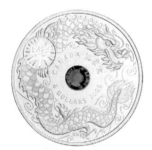

2009 Maple of Wisdom

Date	Description	Buying Price	Date	Description	Buying Price
2004	Great Grizzly	30.00	2007	Trade in Ancient China	20.00
2005	Railway Bridge	20.00	2007	Maple of Long Life	20.00
2005	Chinese Memorial	20.00	2009	Maple of Wisdom	20.00

10 DOLLAR SILVER COINS

2005 Year of the Veteran

2006 Pope John Paul II

2006 Fortress of Louisbourg

Date	Description	Buying Price
2005	Year of the Veteran	18.00
2006	Pope John Paul II	18.00

Date	Description	Buying Price
2006	Fortress of Louisbourg	18.00

15 DOLLAR SILVER COINS
Olympic Centennial Coins

Olympic Sports Reverse
Speed Skater, Pole Vaulter,
Gymnast

Olympic Spirit Reverse

Date	Description	Buying Price
1992	Sports	15.00

Date	Description	Buying Price
1992	Spirit of the Generations	15.00

15 DOLLAR SILVER COINS

CHINESE LUNAR CALENDAR COINS

1998 Year of the Tiger

1999 Year of the Rabbit

2000 Year of the Dragon

2001 Year of the Snake

2002 Year of the Horse

2003 Year of the Ram

2004 Year of the Monkey

2005 Year of the Rooster

2006 Year of the Dog

Date	Description	Buying Price	Date	Description	Buying Price
1998	Tiger	250.00	2003	Ram	40.00
1999	Rabbit	25.00	2004	Monkey	75.00
2000	Dragon	65.00	2005	Rooster	55.00
2001	Snake	25.00	2006	Dog	40.00
2002	Horse	40.00			

15 DOLLAR SILVER COINS

CHINESE LUNAR CALENDAR COINS

2007 Year of the Pig   2008 Year of the Rat   2009 Year of the Ox

Date	Description	Buying Price	Date	Description	Buying Price
2007	Pig	40.00	2009	Ox	40.00
2008	Rat	40.00			

REVERSE VIGNETTES OF ROYALTY SERIES

Obverse   Victoria   Edward VII

George V   George VI   Elizabeth II

Date	Description	Buying Price	Date	Description	Buying Price
2008	Victoria	40.00	2009	George VI	40.00
2008	Edward VII	40.00	2009	Ellizabeth II	40.00
2008	George V	40.00			

20 DOLLAR SILVER COINS
CALGARY 1988 OLYMPIC WINTER GAMES

The XV Winter Olympic Games were held in Calgary, February 13th to 29th, 1988. Ten different $20 silver coins were issued to commemorate this event. The coins weigh 34.107 grams, the composition is .925 silver and .075 copper, and they were issued in proof singles or proof sets in one or two coin display cases. Incorporated into the design of these coins are the letters "XV OLYMPIC WINTER GAMES - XVes JEUX OLYMPIQUE D'HIVER" impressed into the edge. During the striking of these coins at the Royal Canadian Mint, the impressed procedures were skipped on some series resulting in the edge lettering being missed on four known coins, resulting in varieties.

FIRST SERIES

Downhill Skiing

Speed Skating

SECOND SERIES

Hockey

Biathalon

THIRD SERIES

Cross-Country Skiing

Free-Style Skiing

20 DOLLAR SILVER COINS

FOURTH SERIES

Figure Skating

Curling

FIFTH SERIES

Ski Jumping

Bobsleigh

Date	Description	Buying Single	Buying Set
1985	Downhill Skiiing	20.00	
1985	Speed Skating	20.00	40.00
1985	Speed Skating, no edge lettering	100.00	
1986	Hockey	20.00	
1986	Hockey, no edge lettering	100.00	
1986	Biathalon	20.00	40.00
1986	Biathalon, no edge lettering	100.00	
1986	Cross-Country Skiing	20.00	
1986	Free-Style Skiing	20.00	40.00
1986	Free-Style Skiing, no edge lettering	100.00	
1987	Figure Skating	20.00	
1987	Curling	20.00	40.00
1987	Ski Jumping	20.00	
1987	Bobsleigh	20.00	40.00

Note: Single coins and sets, except the varieties, are priced at face value. A dealer may discount the face value to compensate for their required margin.

20 DOLLAR SILVER COINS

AVIATION FIRST SERIES 1990 - 1994

Canada's aviation heroes and their achievements are commemorated on this first series of twenty dollar sterling-silver coins. The series is made up of ten coins, which were issued two per year over five years. For the first time, each coin design contains a 24-karat-gold-covered oval cameo portrait of the aviation hero commemorated. A maximum of 50,000 of each coin was offered for sale.

Coin No. 1
Anson and Harvard /
Robert Leckie

Coin No. 2
Avro Lancaster /
J. E. Fauquier

Coin No. 3
A. E. A. Silver Dart / F. W. Baldwin
and J. A. D. McCurdy

Coin No. 4
de Havilland Beaver /
Phillip C. Garratt

Coin No. 5
Curtiss JN-4 (Canuck) /
Sir F. W. Baillie

Coin No. 6
de Havilland Gypsy Moth /
Murton A. Seymour

20 DOLLAR SILVER COINS

AVIATION FIRST SERIES 1990 - 1994 (cont.)

Coin No. 7
Fairchild 71C / J. A. Richardson

Coin No. 8
Super Electra / Z. L. Leigh

Coin No. 9
Curtiss HS-2L / Stuart Graham

Coin No. 10
Vickers Vedette / T. Reid

Date	Coin No.	Description	Buying Price
1990	1	Anson and Harvard / Leckie	20.00
1990	2	Lancaster / Fauquier	35.00
1991	3	Silver Dart / Baldwin, McCurdy	20.00
1991	4	Beaver / Garratt	20.00
1992	5	Curtiss / Baille	20.00
1992	6	Gypsy Moth / Seymour	20.00
1993	7	Fairchild / Richardson	20.00
1993	8	Super Electra / Leigh	20.00
1994	9	Curtiss / Graham	20.00
1994	10	Vedette / Reid	20.00

20 DOLLAR SILVER COINS

AVIATION SECOND SERIES 1995 - 1999

This second series of aviation coins celebrates "Powered Flight in Canada – Beyond World War II." As with the first series, it was made up of ten coins to be issued two per year over five years. Each coin design contains a 24-karat-gold-covered oval cameo portrait of the pilot, engineers or designers of the aircrafts. A maximum of 50,000 of each coin was offered for sale.

Coin No. 11
The Fleet 80 Canuck / Noury

Coin No. 12
DHC-1 Chipmunk / Bannock

Coin No. 13
CF-100 Canuck / Zurakowski

Coin No. 14
CF-105 Arrow / Chamberlain

Date	Coin No.	Description	Buying Price
1995	11	Fleet 80 Canuck / Noury	20.00
1995	12	DHC-1 Chipmunk / Bannock	20.00
1996	13	CF-100 Canuck / Zurakowski	22.00
1996	14	CF-105 Arrow / Chamberlin	45.00

20 DOLLAR SILVER COINS

AVIATION SECOND SERIES 1995 - 1999 (cont.)

Coin No. 15
Canadian F-86 Sabre /
Fern Villeneuve

Coin No. 16
Canadair CT-114 Tutor /
Edward Higgins

Coin No. 17
CP-107 Argus /
William S. Longhurst

Coin No. 18
CL-215 Waterbomber /
Paul Gagnon

Coin No. 19
DHC-6 Twin Otter / G. A. Neal

Coin No. 20
DHC-8 Dash 8 / R. H. Fowler

Date	Coin No.	Description	Buying Price
1997	15	F-86 Sabre / Villeneuve	20.00
1997	16	CT-114 Tutor / Higgin	20.00
1998	17	CP-107 Argus / Longhurst	20.00
1998	18	CL-215 Waterbomber / Gagnon	30.00
1999	19	DHC-6 Twin Otter / Neal	35.00
1999	20	DHC-8 Dash 8 / Fowler	45.00

20 DOLLAR SILVER COINS

LAND, SEA AND RAIL 2000 - 2002

Coin No. 1
H. S. Taylor Steam Buggy

Coin No. 2
The Bluenose

Coin No. 3
The Toronto

Coin No. 4
The Russel

Coin No. 5
The Marco Polo

Coin No. 6
The Scotia

Coin No. 7
The Gray-Dort

Coin No. 8
The William Lawrence

Coin No. 9
The D-10 Locomotive

Date	Coin No.	Description	Buying Price
2000	1	H. S. Taylor Steam Buggy	20.00
2000	2	The Bluenose	75.00
2000	3	The Toronto	20.00
2001	4	The Russel	20.00
2001	5	The Marco Polo	20.00
2001	6	The Scotia	20.00
2002	7	The Gray-Dort	20.00
2002	8	The William Lawrence	20.00
2002	9	The D-10 Locomotive	20.00

20 DOLLAR SILVER COINS

LAND, SEA AND RAIL 2003

Coin No. 10
HMCS Bras d'or

Coin No. 11
CNR FA-1 Diesel Electric

Coin No. 12
Bricklin SV-1

Date	Coin No.	Description	Buying Price
2003	10	HMCS Bras d'or	20.00
2003	11	C.N.R. FA-1 Diesel Electric Locomotive	20.00
2003	12	Bricklin SV-1	20.00

NATURAL WONDERS COLLECTION

Coin No. 1 Niagara Falls

Coin No. 2 Rocky Mountains

Coin No. 3 Icebergs

Coin No. 4 Northern Lights

Coin No. 5 Hopewell Rocks

Coin No. 6 Diamonds

Date	Coin No.	Description	Buying Price
2003	1	Niagara Falls	30.00
2003	2	Rocky Mountains	25.00
2004	3	Icebergs	20.00
2004	4	Northern Lights	25.00
2005	5	Hopewell Rocks	20.00
2005	6	Diamonds	20.00

20 DOLLAR SILVER COINS

TALL SHIPS COLLECTION

Coin No. 1 Three-Masted Ship   Coin No. 2 Ketch   Coin No. 3 Brigantine

Date	Coin No.	Description	Buying Price
2005	1	Three-masted Ship, Hologram	20.00
2006	2	Ketch, Hologram	20.00
2007	3	Brigantine, Hologram	20.00

NATIONAL PARKS SERIES

Coin No. 1
North Pacific
Rim

Coin No. 2
Mingan
Archipelago

Coin No. 3 Georgian Bay   Coin No. 4 Nahanni Park   Coin No. 5 Jasper National Park

Date	Coin No.	Description	Buying Price
2005	1	North Pacific Rim National Park Reserve	20.00
2005	2	Mingan Archipelago National Park Reserve	20.00
2006	3	Georgian Bay Islands National Park	20.00
2006	4	Nahanni National Park Reserve	20.00
2006	5	Jasper National Park	20.00

20 DOLLAR SILVER COINS

CANADIAN ARCHITECTURAL COLLECTION

Coin No. 1 Notre Dame Basilica   Coin No. 2 CN Tower   Coin No. 3 Pengrowth Saddledome

Date	Coin No.	Description	Buying Price
2006	1	Notre Dame Basilica, Hologram	20.00
2006	2	30th Anniversary CN Tower, Hologram	25.00
2006	3	Pengrowth Saddledome, Hologram	20.00

CRYSTAL SNOWFLAKES

2007 Crystal Snowflake   2008 Crystal Snowflake   2009 Crystal Snowflake

Date	Description	Buying Price
2007	Crystal Snowflake, Aquamarine	30.00
2007	Crystal Snowflake, Irridescent	30.00
2008	Crystal Snowflake, Amethyst	30.00
2008	Crystal Snowflake, Sapphire	30.00
2009	Crystal Snowflake, Blue	30.00
2009	Crystal Snowflake, Pink	30.00

20 DOLLAR SILVER COINS

2007 Polar Year   2007 Holiday Sleigh Ride   2008 Holiday Carols

2008 Royal Hudson   2009 The Jubilee   2009 Summer Moon Mask

Date	Description	Buying Price
2007	125th Anniversary of the First International Polar Year	30.00
2007	Holiday Sleigh Ride	30.00
2008	Holiday Carols	30.00
2009	Royal Hudson	30.00
2009	Jubilee Locomotive	30.00
2009	The Jubilee	30.00
2009	Summer Moon Mask	30.00

CANADIAN TRADES COLLECTION

2008 Agriculture   2009 Coal Mining

Date	Description	Buying Price
2008	Agriculture	30.00
2009	Coal Mining	30.00

20 DOLLAR SILVER COINS

2008-2009 HOCKEY SEASON (Goalie Masks)

Calgary Flames   Edmonton Oilers   Montreal Canadiens

Ottawa Senators   Toronto Maple Leafs   Vancouver Canucks

Date	Description	Buying Price
2009	Calgary Flames	30.00
2009	Edmonton Oilers	30.00
2009	Montreal Canadiens	30.00
2009	Ottawa Senators	30.00
2009	Toronto Maple Leafs	30.00
2009	Vancouver Canucks	30.00

25 DOLLAR SILVER COINS

VANCOUVER 2010 OLYMPIC WINTER GAMES

Coin. No. 1
Curling

Coin No. 2
Ice Hockey

Coin No. 3
Athletes' Pride

Coin. No. 4
Biathlon

Coin No. 5
Alpine Skiing

Coin No. 6
Snowboarding

Coin. No. 7
Freestyle Skiing

Coin No. 8
Home of the 2010
Olympic Winter Games

Coin No.
9 Figure Skating

Date	Coin No.	Description	Buying Price
2007	1	Curling	30.00
2007	2	Ice Hockey	30.00
2007	3	Athletes' Pride	30.00
2007	4	Biathlon	30.00
2007	5	Alpine Skiing	30.00
2008	6	Snowboarding	30.00
2008	7	Freestyle Skiing	30.00
2008	8	Home of the 2010 Olympic Winter Games	30.00
2008	9	Figure Skating	30.00

25 DOLLAR SILVER COINS

VANCOUVER 2010 OLYMPIC WINTER GAMES

Coin. No. 10
Bobsleigh

Coin No. 11
Speed Skating

Coin No. 12
Cross Country Skiing

Coin. No. 13
Olympic Spirit

Coin No. 14
Skeleton

Coin No. 15
Ski Jumping

Date	Coin No.	Description	Buying Price
2008	10	Bobsleigh	30.00
2009	11	Speed Skating	30.00
2009	12	Cross Country Skiing	30.00
2009	13	Olympic Spirit	30.00
2009	14	Skeleton	30.00
2009	15	Ski Jumping	30.00

30 DOLLAR SILVER COINS

Welcome Figure Totem Pole

5th Anniversary Canadarm

Dog Sled

National War Memorial

Beaumont-Hamel Newfoundland Memorial

Canadian National Vimy Memorial

Panoramic Photography in Canada

IMAX

International Year of Astronomy

Date	Description	Buying Price
2006	Welcome Figure Totem Pole	25.00
2006	5th Anniversary Canadarm	30.00
2006	Dog Sled	40.00
2006	National War Memorial	40.00
2006	Beaumont-Hamel Newfoundland Memorial	35.00
2007	Canadian National Vimy Memorial	35.00
2007	Panoramic Photography in Canada	30.00
2008	IMAX	30.00
2009	International Year of Astronomy	40.00

50 DOLLAR SILVER COINS

The Four Seasons

Queen's 60th Wedding Anniversary

Date	Description	Buying Price
2006	The Four Seasons	200.00
2007	Queen's 60th Wedding Anniversary	125.00
2008	100th Anniversary of the Royal Canadian Mint	175.00
2009	150th Anniversary of Parliament	200.00

250 DOLLAR SILVER COINS

VANCOUVER 2010 OLYMPIC WINTER GAMES

Early Canada

Towards Confederation

Date	Description	Buying Price
2007	Early Canada	600.00
2008	Towards Confederation	600.00
2009	The Canada of Today	500.00
2010	Surviving the Flood	500.00

Note: Coins illustrated smaller than actual size.

1 DOLLAR GOLD COIN

| 2006 | 2007 | 2008 |

Date	Description	Buying Price
2006	Gold Louis	50.00
2007	Gold Louis	50.00
2008	Gold Louis	50.00

20 DOLLAR GOLD COIN

Date	Description	Buying Price
1967	Centennial Confederation	500.00

50 DOLLAR GOLD COIN

60th Anniv. End WWII

Date	Description	Buying Price
2005	60th Anniv. End WWII	285.00

75 DOLLAR GOLD COINS

POPE JOHN PAUL II

Date	Description	Buying Price
2005	Pope John Paul II	400.00

Note: Prices in this book are based on gold and silver values as of June 11th, 2010, and Canadian /United States foreign currency rates of the same day.

VANCOUVER 2010 OLYMPIC WINTER GAMES

2007 Obv.

2007 R.C.M.P.

2007 Athletes' Pride

2007 Canada Geese

2008 Obv.

2008 Four Host Nations

2008 Home of the Games

2008 Inukshuk

2009 Obv.

2009 Wolf

2009 Olympic Spirit

2009 Moose

Date	Description	Buying Price	Date	Description	Buying Price
2007	R.C.M.P.	225.00	2008	Inukshuk	225.00
2007	Athletes' Pride	225.00	2009	Wolf	225.00
2007	Canada Geese	225.00	2009	Olympic Spirit	225.00
2008	Four Host Nations	225.00	2009	Moose	225.00
2008	Home of the 2010 Games	225.00			

100 DOLLAR GOLD COINS

Canada issued the first one-hundred-dollar gold coin in 1976 to commemorate the Montreal Olympic Games. In that year two qualities and proportions of fineness were released; uncirculated coins were .585 fine (14 karat), and proof coins were .916 fine (22 karat). From 1976 to 1986, only proof quality coins with a fineness of .916 were issued. In 1987 the quality remained the same (proof), but the fineness of the coin was altered to .583 fine, or 14 karat, again.

IMPORTANT

Proof coins must be in mint-state condition. Mishandled, mounted or damaged coins are discounted from the prices listed. The buying price for gold coins is tied to the market price of gold. Any movement in the gold price will result in a corresponding price movement for these coins.

1976 - 14kt   1976 - 22 kt

1977   1978   1979   1980

1981   1982   1983   1984

Date	Description	Fineness	Buying Price	Date	Description	Fineness	Buying Price
1976	14 kt Olympic	.583	240.00	1980	Arctic Territories	.916	475.00
1976	22 kt Olympic	.916	475.00	1981	"O Canada"	.916	475.00
1977	Jubilee	.916	475.00	1982	Constitution	.916	475.00
1978	Unity	.916	475.00	1983	Gilbert's Landing	.916	475.00
1979	Year of the Child	.916	475.00	1984	Voyage of Discovery	.916	475.00

100 DOLLAR GOLD COINS

1985	1986	1987	1988
1989	1990	1991	1992
1993	1994	1995	1996
1997	1998	1999	2000

Date	Description	Fineness	Buying Price	Date	Description	Fineness	Buying Price
1985	National Parks	.916	475.00	1993	Horseless Carriage	.583	240.00
1986	Peace	.916	475.00	1994	The Home Front	.583	240.00
1987	Calgary Olympics	.583	240.00	1995	Louisbourg	.583	240.00
1988	Bowhead Whale	.583	240.00	1996	Klondike Gold Rush	.583	240.00
1989	Ste. Marie	.583	240.00	1997	Bell	.583	240.00
1990	Literacy Year	.583	240.00	1998	Insulin	.583	240.00
1991	Empress of India	.583	240.00	1999	Newfoundland	.583	240.00
1992	Montreal	.583	240.00	2000	Northwest Passage	.583	240.00

100 DOLLAR GOLD COINS

2001   2002   2003   2004

2005   2006   2007   2008

2009

Date	Description	Fineness	Buying Price	Date	Description	Fineness	Buying Price
2001	Library	.583	240.00	2006	Hockey	.583	215.00
2002	Oil Well	.583	240.00	2007	Dominion of Canada	.583	215.00
2003	Wheat	.583	240.00	2008	Fraser River	.583	215.00
2004	Seaway	.583	215.00	2009	Nunavut	.583	215.00
2005	Supreme Court	.583	215.00				

150 DOLLAR GOLD COINS

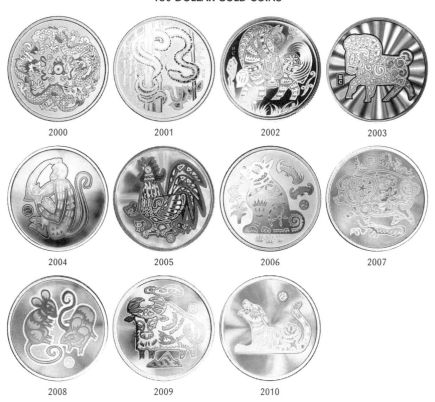

2000	2001	2002	2003
2004	2005	2006	2007
2008	2009	2010	

Date	Description	Buying Price	Date	Description	Buying Price
2000	Year of the Dragon	750.00	2006	Year of the Dog	275.00
2001	Year of the Snake	275.00	2007	Year of the Pig	275.00
2002	Year of the Horse	275.00	2008	Year of the Rat	275.00
2003	Year of the Ram	275.00	2009	Year of the Ox	275.00
2004	Year of the Monkey	275.00	2010	Year of the Tiger	275.00
2005	Year of the Rooster	275.00			

175 DOLLAR GOLD COIN

Date	Description	Buying Price
1992	Olympic	475.00

200 DOLLAR GOLD COINS

22 KARAT (.916) GOLD

Date	Description	Buying Price	Date	Description	Buying Price
1990	Canada Flag	475.00	1998	White Buffalo	475.00
1991	A National Passion	475.00	1999	Mikmaq Butterfly	475.00
1992	Niagara Falls	475.00	2000	Mother and Child	475.00
1993	RCMP	475.00	2001	Cornelius Krieghoff	475.00
1994	Anne of Green Gables	475.00	2002	Tom Thomson	475.00
1995	Sugar Bush	475.00	2003	Lionel Fitzgerald	475.00
1996	Transcontinental	475.00	2004	Alfred Pellan	450.00
1997	Haida	475.00	2005	Fur Traders	450.00

200 DOLLAR GOLD COINS

22 KARAT (.916) GOLD

2006   2007

2008   2009

2010

Date	Description	Buying Price
2006	Timber Trade	450.00
2007	Fishing Trade	450.00
2008	Agriculture Trade	450.00
2009	Coal Mining	450.00
2010	First Canadian Olympic Gold	450.00

250 DOLLAR GOLD COINS

14 KARAT (.583) GOLD

2006 Obv.

2006 Dog Sled Team

Date	Description	Buying Price
2006	Dog Sled Team	800.00

103

300 DOLLAR GOLD COINS

14 KARAT (.583) GOLD, LARGE SIZE (50 mm)

2002 Jubilee / Triple Cameo

2003 Great Seal of Canada

2004 Arms of Canada / Quadruple Cameo

2005 The 1870 Shinplaster

2006 The 1900 Shinplaster

2006 The 1923 Shinplaster

Date	Description	Buying Price	Date	Description	Buying Price
2002	Jubilee / Triple Cameo Portraits	1,100.00	2005	The 1870 Shinplaster	1,100.00
2003	Great Seal of Canada	1,100.00	2006	The 1900 Shinplaster	1,100.00
2004	Quadruple Cameo Portraits	1,100.00	2007	The 1923 Shinplaster	1,100.00

300 DOLLAR GOLD COINS

14 KARAT (.583) GOLD, LARGE SIZE (50 mm)

2006 Crystal Snowflake

2006 80th Birthday Queen Elizabeth II

2007 Olympic Ideals

2008 Competition

2007 Four Seasons Moon Mask

2008 Provincial Arms

Date	Description	Buying Price	Date	Description	Buying Price
2006	Crystal Snowflake	1,100.00	2007	Four Seasons Moon Mask	1,100.00
2006	80th Birthday Elizabeth II	1,100.00	2008	Competition	1,100.00
2007	Olympic Ideals	1,100.00	2008	Provincial Arms	1,100.00

300 DOLLAR GOLD COINS

14 KARAT (.583) GOLD, SMALL SIZE (40 mm)

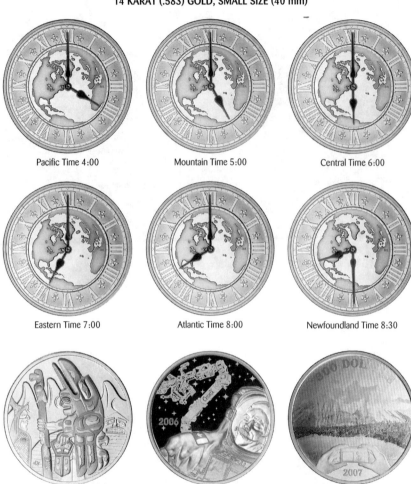

Pacific Time 4:00	
Mountain Time 5:00	
Central Time 6:00	
Eastern Time 7:00	
Atlantic Time 8:00	
Newfoundland Time 8:30	
Welcome Figure Totem Pole	
5th Anniv. Canadarm	
2007 Panorama Photography	

Date	Description	Buying Price		Date	Description	Buying Price
2005	Pacific Time 4:00	800.00		2005	Newfoundland Time 8:30	800.00
2005	Mountain Time 5:00	800.00		2005	Welcome Figure Totem Pole	800.00
2005	Central Time 6:00	800.00		2006	5th Anniv. Canadarm	800.00
2005	Eastern Time 7:00	800.00		2007	Panorama Photography	800.00
2005	Atlantic Time 8:00	800.00				

Note: Images on page 104 to 107 are shown smaller than actual size.

350 DOLLAR GOLD COINS
24 Karat (.99999) GOLD

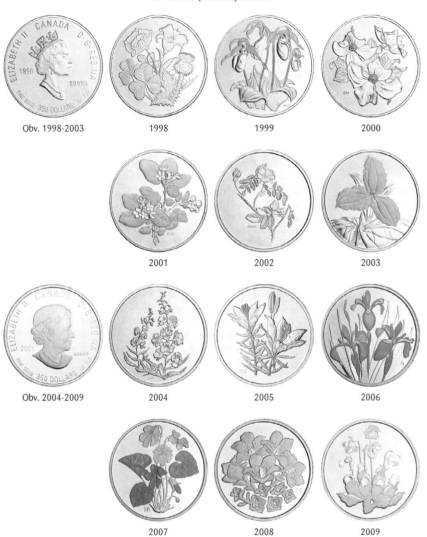

Obv. 1998-2003   1998   1999   2000

2001   2002   2003

Obv. 2004-2009   2004   2005   2006

2007   2008   2009

Date	Description	Buying Price	Date	Description	Buying Price
1998	90th Anniv. R.C.M.	1,175.00	2004	Fireweed	1,175.00
1999	Golden Slipper	1,175.00	2005	Western Red Lily	1,175.00
2000	Pacific Dogwood	1,175.00	2006	Iris Versicolor	1,175.00
2001	Mayflower	1,175.00	2007	Purple Violet	1,175.00
2002	Wild Rose	1,175.00	2008	Purple Saxifrage	1,175.00
2003	Trillium	1,175.00	2009	Pitcher Plant	1,175.00

PALLADIUM COINS

FIFTY DOLLARS

BIG AND LITTLE BEAR CONSTELLATIONS, 2006

Spring

Summer

Autumn

Winter

Date	Description	Buying Price
2006	Spring	400.00
2006	Summer	400.00
2006	Autumn	400.00
2006	Winter	400.00

PROOF PLATINUM COINS

1990 Polar Bears   1991 Snowy Owls   1992 Cougars   1993 Arctic Foxes

1994 Otters   1995 Canada Lynx   1996 Peregrine Falcon   1997 Wood Bison

1998 Grey Wolf   1999 Muskox   2000 Pronghorn   2001 Harlequin Duck

2002 Great Blue Heron   2003 Atlantic Walrus   2004 Grizzly Bear

Date	Description	Buying Price	Date	Description	Buying Price
1990	Polar Bear Set	2,250.00	1997	Wood Bison $30	100.00
1991	Snowy Owl Set	2,250.00	1997	Wood Bison $150	550.00
1992	Cougar Set	2,250.00	1998	Grey Wolf Set	2,250.00
1993	Arctic Foxes Set	2,250.00	1998	Grey Wolf $30	100.00
1994	Sea Otters Set	2,250.00	1998	Grey Wolf $150	550.00
1995	Canada Lynx Set	2,250.00	1999	Muskox Set	2,250.00
1995	Canada Lynx $30	100.00	1999	Muskox $30	100.00
1995	Canada Lynx $150	550.00	2000	Pronghorn Set	2,250.00
1996	Peregrine Falcon Set	2,250.00	2001	Harlequin Duck Set	2,250.00
1996	Peregrine Falcon $30	100.00	2002	Great Blue Heron Set	2,250.00
1996	Peregrine Falcon $150	550.00	2003	Atlantic Walrus Set	2,250.00
1997	Wood Bison Set	2,250.00	2004	Grizzly Bear Set	2,250.00

Note: The Platinum Proof Set contains four coins: $300., $150., $75. and $30. coins.

COLLECTOR SETS

Listed on this and the following page are the Collector sets of coins issued by the Royal Canadian Mint between the years 1954 and 2005.

SIX COIN PROOF-LIKE AND BRILLIANT UNCIRCULATED SETS

SILVER 6-COIN PROOF-LIKE SETS

Date	Description	Buying Price
1954	Voyageur	325.00
1955	Voyageur	225.00
1955	Arnprior	300.00
1956	Voyageur	135.00
1957	Voyageur	80.00
1958	British Columbia	65.00
1959	Voyageur	30.00
1960	Voyageur	20.00
1961	Voyageur	12.00
1962	Voyageur	12.00
1963	Voyageur	12.00
1964	Charlottetown	12.00
1965	Voyageur	12.00
1966	Voyageur	12.00
1967	Centennial	12.00

NICKEL 6-COIN BRILLIANT UNCIRCULATED SETS

Date	Description	Buying Price
1968	Voyageur	2.00
1969	Voyageur	2.00
1970	Manitoba	2.00
1971	British Columbia	2.00
1972	Voyageur	2.00
1973	R.C.M.P., Small Bust	2.00
1973	R.C.M.P., Large Bust	150.00
1974	Winnipeg	2.00
1975	Voyageur	2.00
1976	Voyageur	2.00
1977	Voyageur	2.00
1978	Voyageur	2.00
1979	Voyageur	2.00
1980	Voyageur	2.00
1981	Voyageur	2.00
1982	Voyageur	2.00
1983	Voyageur	2.50

NICKEL 6-COIN BRILLIANT UNCIRCULATED SETS

Date	Description	Buying Price
1984	Voyageur	2.50
1985	Voyageur	2.50
1986	Voyageur	2.50
1987	Voyageur	2.50
1988	Loon	2.50
1989	Loon	4.00
1990	Loon	4.00
1991	Loon	10.00
1992	Loon	5.00
1993	Loon	2.00
1994	Loon	2.50
1995	Loon	2.50
1996	Loon	10.00

"OH CANADA!" NICKEL 6-COIN SETS

Date	Description	Buying Price
1994	Loon	4.00
1995	Loon	4.00
1996	Loon	7.00

"BUNDLE OF JOY/TINY TREASURES" NICKEL 6-COIN SETS

Date	Description	Buying Price
1995	Loon	6.00
1996	Loon	6.00

SEVEN COIN BRILLIANT UNCIRCULATED SETS

BRILLIANT UNCIRCULATED SETS

Date	Description	Buying Price
1997	Loon/Polar Bear	4.00
1998W	Loon/Polar Bear	8.00
1998	Loon/Polar Bear	8.00
1999	Loon/Polar Bear	4.00
1999	Loon/Nunavut	4.00
2000	Loon/Polar Bear	4.00
2000W	Loon/Polar Bear	4.00
2000	Loon/Polar Bears	4.00
2001P	Loon/Polar Bear	4.00
1952-2002P	Loon/Polar Bear	8.00
1952-2002P	Special	4.00
2003P	Loon/Polar Bear	10.00
2003WP	Special	10.00
2004P	Loon/Polar Bear	10.00
2005P	Loon/Polar Bear	8.00
2006P	Loon/Polar Bear	8.00
2007	Loon/Polar Bear	9.00
2008	Loon/Polar Bear	9.00
2009	Loon/Polar Bear	9.00

"BUNDLE OF JOY/TINY TREASURES" SETS

Date	Description	Buying Price
1997	Loon/Polar Bear	5.00
1998	Loon/Polar Bear	5.00
1998W	Loon/Polar Bear	5.00
1999	Loon/Polar Bear	5.00
2000	Loon/Polar Bear	5.00
2000W	Loon/Polar Bear	5.00
2001	Loon/Polar Bears	5.00

"OH CANADA!" SETS

Date	Description	Buying Price
1997	Flying Loon/Polar Bear	15.00
1998	Loon/Polar Bear	6.00
1998W	Loon/Polar Bear	8.00
1999	Loon/Polar Bear	5.00
2000	Loon/Polar Bear	5.00
2000W	Loon/Polar Bear	5.00
2001P	Loon/Polar Bear	5.00
2002P	Loon/Polar Bear	7.00
2003P	Loon/Polar Bear	7.00
2004P	Loon/Polar Bear	8.00
2005P	Loon/Polar Bear	8.00
2006P	Loon/Polar Bear	8.00
2007	Loon/Polar Bear	8.00
2008	Loon/Polar Bear	8.00
2009	Loon/Polar Bear	8.00

"GIFT" SETS

Date	Description	Buying Price
2001P	Loon/Polar Bear	6.00
2002P	Loon/Polar Bear	6.00
2003P	Loon/Polar Bear	8.00
2004P	Loon/Polar Bear	8.00
2005P	Loon/Polar Bear	8.00
2006P	Loon/Polar Bear	8.00
2007	Loon/Polar Bear	8.00
2008	Loon/Polar Bear	8.00
2009	Loon/Polar Bear	8.00

Note: Gifts Sets are found in different categories: Birthday, Congratulations, Graduations, Weddings.

SPECIAL EDITION BRILLIANT UNCIRCULATED SETS

7-COIN SETS

Date	Description	Buying Price
2002P	Accession	7.00
2003WP	Coronation	7.00
2006	10th Anniversary	7.00

8-COIN SETS

Date	Description	Buying Price
2005P	Alberta Centenary	8.00
2005P	Saskatchewan Centenary	8.00

11-COIN SETS

Date	Description	Buying Price
2007	Winter Olympics	10.00
2008	Winter Olympics	10.00
2009	Winter Olympics	10.00
2009	Golden Moments	10.00

SPECIMEN SETS

SPECIMEN 7-COIN SETS (Double Cent Sets)

Date	Description	Buying Price
1971	Voyageur	3.00
1972	Voyageur	3.00
1973	Voyageur/RCMP, Small Bust	3.00
1973	Voyageur/RCMP, Large Bust	125.00
1974	Voyaguer	3.00
1975	Voyageur	3.00
1976	Voyageur	3.00
1977	Voyageur	3.00
1978	Voyageur	3.00
1979	Voyageur	3.00
1980	Voyageur	3.00

6-COIN SETS (One Cent to One Dollar)

Date	Description	Buying Price
1981	Voyageur	3.50
1982	Voyageur	3.50
1983	Voyageur	3.50
1984	Voyageur	3.50
1985	Voyageur	3.50
1986	Voyageur	3.50
1987	Voyageur	3.50
1988	Loon	3.50
1989	Loon	4.00

SPECIMEN 6-COIN SETS (One Cent to One Dollar)

Date	Description	Buying Price
1990	Loon	4.00
1991	Loon	16.00
1992	Loon	7.00
1993	Loon	4.00
1994	Loon	4.00
1995	Loon	4.00
1996	Loon	10.00

SPECIMEN 7-COIN SETS
(One Cent to Two Dollars)

Date	Description	Buying Price
1997	Flying Loon/Polar Bear	15.00
1998	Loon/Polar Bear	6.00
1999	Loon/Polar Bear	6.00
2000	Loon/Polar Bear	6.00
2000	Loon/Polar Bears	6.00
2001P	Loon/Polar Bear	6.00
2002P	Loon Family/Polar Bear	10.00
2003P	Loon/Polar Bear	10.00
2004P	Canada Goose/Polar Bear	20.00
2005P	Puffin/Polar Bear	25.00
2006P	Snowy Owl/Polar Bear	25.00
2007	Trumpeter Swans/ Polar Bear	20.00
2008	Eider Duck/Polar Bear	20.00
2009	Great Heron/Polar Bear	20.00

PROOF SETS

PROOF 7-COIN SETS

Date	Description	Buying Price
1971	British Columbia	8.00
1972	Voyageur	15.00
1973	R.C.M.P., Small Bust	8.00
1973	R.C.M.P., Large Bust	150.00
1974	Winnipeg	8.00
1975	Calgary	8.00
1976	Parliament	8.00
1977	Jubilee	8.00
1978	Commonwealth Games	8.00
1979	Griffon	8.00
1980	Polar Bear	10.00
1981	Trans Canada	10.00
1982	Regina	8.00
1983	University Games	8.00
1984	Toronto	10.00
1985	National Parks	10.00
1986	Vancouver	10.00
1987	Davis Straits	10.00
1988	Ironworks	10.00
1989	MacKenzie River	12.00
1990	Henry Kelsey	14.00

PROOF 7-COIN SETS

Date	Description	Buying Price
1991	Frontenac	25.00
1992	Stagecoach	20.00
1993	Hockey	13.00
1994	RCMP	15.00
1994	RCMP Red Box	15.00
1995	Hudson's Bay	15.00
1995	Hudson's Bay Red Box	15.00
1996	John McIntosh	20.00

PROOF 8-COIN SETS

Date	Description	Buying Price
1997	Canada/Russia Hockey	20.00
1998	RCMP 125th Anniversary	25.00
1999	Juan Perez	35.00
2000	Discovery	30.00
2001	Ballet	18.00
2002	Jubilee	30.00
2003	Cobalt	30.00
2004	Ste Croix	40.00
2005	Canadian Flag	50.00
2006	Victoria Cross	40.00
2007	Thayendanegea	40.00
2008	Quebec	40.00
2009	Flight in Canada	40.00

MAPLE LEAF BULLION COINS

The Maple Leaf gold coins were first produced in 1979, the fractional or small sizes three years later in 1982, and the half-ounce size in 1986. In 1988 the four sizes; $5.00, $10.00, $20.00 and $50.00, of platinum were added. Expanding the range in 1993, $1.00 gold and platinum coins were issued, and again in 1994 $2.00 coins were placed on the market.

The price of Maple Leaf bullion coins is based on the spot market price in Canadian dollars on the day of purchase, times their precious metal content, less a small handling charge.

| $50 | $20 | $10 | $5 |

COIN SPECIFICATIONS

Denomination	Description	Content	Weight Tr. Oz.
$1	1/20 Maple	Gold or platinum	.050
$2	1/15 Maple	Gold or platinum	.667
$5	1/10 Maple	Gold or platinum	.100
$10	1/4 Maple	Gold or platinum	.250
$20	1/2 Maple	Gold or platinum	.500
$50	Maple	Gold or platinum	1.00
$5	Maple	Silver	1.00
$50	10 Maple	Silver	10.00

MAPLE LEAF PROOF BULLION ISSUES OF 1989

To commemorate the tenth anniversary of the Maple Leaf bullion program, the Royal Canadian Mint, in 1989, issued a series of proof condition silver, gold and platinum coins, individually and in sets. The single coins and sets were packaged in solid maple presentation cases with brown velvet liners.

Type	Description	Buying Price
Sets	Gold 4 coins: 1, 1/2, 1/4, 1/10 ounce maple	1,850.00
	Platinum 4 coins: 1, 1/2, 1/4, 1/10 ounce maple	2,350.00
	Gold and Platinum 1/10 ounce maple each, Silver 1 ounce Maple, 3 coins	275.00
	Gold, Platinum and Silver 3 coins: 1 ounce maple each	2,400.00
Singles	Gold, One Maple	1,100.00
	Silver, One Maple	20.00

PAPER MONEY OF CANADA

PROVINCE OF CANADA

1866 ISSUES

Denom.	Issue Date	Buying Price	Denom.	Issue Date	Buying Price
$1	1866	1,200.00	$10	1866	7,500.00
$2	1866	2,000.00	$20	1866	10,000.00
$5	1866	4,500.00	$50	1866	15,000.00

CANADA

1870 ISSUES

Plain	Series Letter A	Series Letter B

Denom.	Issue Date	Buying Price	Denom.	Issue Date	Buying Price
25-cent Plain	1870	14.00	25-cent Series B	1870	15.00
25-cent Series A	1870	125.00			

Note: The buying prices listed are for notes in **Very Good (VG)** condition.

1870 ISSUES

Denom.	Issue Date	Variety/Signature	Buying Price
$1	1870	Payable at Montreal or Toronto	500.00
$1	1870	Payable at Halifax	2,000.00
$1	1870	Payable at St. John	2,000.00
$2	1870	Payable at Montreal or Toronto	2,000.00
$2	1870	Payable at Halifax or St. John	3,500.00

1878 ISSUES

Denom.	Issue Date	Variety/Signature	Buying Price
$1	1878	Scalloped Frame, Payable at Montreal or Toronto	375.00
$1	1878	Scalloped Frame, Payable at St. John or Halifax	1,300.00
$1	1878	Lettered Frame, Payable at Montreal or Toronto	150.00
$1	1878	Lettered Frame, Payable at St. John or Halifax	1,500.00
$2	1878	Payable at Montreal or Toronto	1,375.00
$2	1878	Payable at St. John or Halifax	2,250.00

1882 AND 1887 ISSUES

Denom.	Issue Date	Variety/Signature	Buying Price
$4	1882		750.00
$2	1887	Plain,	400.00
$2	1887	Series A	2,000.00

Note: The buying prices listed are for notes in **Very Good (VG)** condition.

1897 AND 1898 ISSUES

| | No "One" 1897 | Inward "One" 1898 | Outward "One" 1898 |

Denom.	Issue Date	Variety/Signature	Buying Price
$1	1897	Green face tint	300.00
$2	1897	Red-brown back	2,500.00
$2	1897	Dark brown back	175.00
$1	1898	Inward "One"	75.00
$1	1898	Outward "One"	60.00

1900 AND 1902 ISSUES

| | "4" on Top | "Four" on Top |

Denom.	Issue Date	Variety/Signature	Buying Price
25-cent	1900	Courtney	3.00
25-cent	1900	Bouville	3.00
25-cent	1900	Saunders	3.00
$4	1900		500.00
$4	1902	"4" on Top	900.00
$4	1902	"Four" on Top	400.00

Note: The buying prices listed are for notes in **Very Good (VG)** condition.

1911 AND 1912 ISSUES

No Seal   Seal over Five   Seal Only

Denom.	Issue Date	Variety/Signature	Buying Price
$1	1911	Green Line or Black Line	45.00
$500	1911		25,000.00
$1,000	1911		25,000.00
$5	1912	No Seal	425.00
$5	1912	Seal over Five	475.00
$5	1912	Seal Only	425.00

1914 AND 1917 ISSUES

Denom.	Issue Date	Variety/Signature	Buying Price
$2	1914	No Seal	65.00
$2	1914	Seal over Two	85.00
$2	1914	Seal Only	65.00
$1	1917	No Seal	30.00
$1	1917	Seal over One	30.00
$1	1917	Black Seal	30.00

Note: The buying prices listed are for notes in **Very Good (VG)** condition.

1923 ISSUES

Denom.	Issue Date	Variety/Signature	Buying Price
25-cent	1923	Hyndman/Saunders	5.00
25-cent	1923	McCavour/Saunders	2.00
25-cent	1923	Campbell/Clark	2.00
$1	1923	Various Colour Seals	20.00
$1	1923	Purple Seal	100.00
$2	1923	Various Colour Seals	30.00
$2	1923	Green Seal	40.00
$2	1923	Bronze Seal	30.00

1924 AND 1925 ISSUES

Denom.	Issue Date	Variety/Signature	Buying Price
$5	1924	Queen Mary	2,200.00
$500	1925	George V	25,000.00
$1,000	1925	Queen Mary	25,000.00

Note: The buying prices listed are for notes in **Very Good (VG)** condition.

BANK OF CANADA

1935 ISSUES

Denom.	Variety	Buying Price	Denom.	Variety	Buying Price
$1	English text	15.00	$20	French text	400.00
$1	French text	35.00	$25	English text	1,250.00
$2	English text	30.00	$25	French text	1,700.00
$2	French text	100.00	$50	English text	900.00
$5	English text	45.00	$50	French text	1,200.00
$5	French text	60.00	$100	English text	600.00
$10	English text	45.00	$100	French text	1,200.00
$10	French text	90.00	$500	English or French	15,000.00
$20	English text	250.00	$1,000	English or French	2,000.00

Note: The buying prices listed are for notes in **Very Good (VG)** condition.

1937 ISSUES

IMPORTANT

| Denom. | Very Fine Buying Prices By Signature | | |
	Osborne	Gordon	Coyne
$1	15.00	5.00	5.00
$2	50.00	15.00	15.00
$5	100.00	15.00	15.00
$10	90.00	11.00	11.00
$20	100.00	22.00	22.00
$50	400.00	60.00	60.00
$100	400.00	100.00	100.00
$1,000	1,500.00	NI	NI

IMPORTANT

The buying prices listed are for notes in **Very Fine (VF)** condition.
- A. The note will have no tears, holes or writing of any kind and will be completely intact.
- B. Evidence of wear may be present along the edges and corners, with no weakness in the design. The corners will not be rounded.
- C. The note may have up to four major creases or folds with broken paper fibres, but no design loss in the creases.

Note: NI - Not issued

1954 ISSUES

"DEVIL'S FACE" PORTRAIT

THE DEVIL'S FACE NOTES

On the earliest notes of the 1954 issue, highlighted areas of the Queen's hair produced the illusion of a leering demonic face behind her ear. This was not the result of an error, nor was it, as some have asserted, the prank of an IRA sympathizer at the bank note company. It was merely the faithful reproduction of the original photograph. The portrait of the Queen with the devil's face outlined in her hair generated almost instant controversy.

ASTERISK NOTES

Asterisk notes are replacement notes, the first being spoiled in printing, cutting, etc., and replaced by an asterisk note. The asterisk is a small star-like symbol which appears before the prefix letters and serial number.

| | Very Fine Buying Price by Signature | | | |
| | Coyne/Towers | | Beattie/Coyne | |
Denom.	Regular	Asterisk	Regular	Asterisk
$1	9.00	600.00	7.00	400.00
$2	20.00	1,200.00	10.00	600.00
$5	25.00	3,000.00	20.00	1,500.00
$10	15.00	1,000.00	12.00	800.00
$20	25.00	1,500.00	25.00	1,200.00
$50	55.00	NI	55.00	NI
$100	110.00	NI	110.00	NI
$1,000	1,500.00	NI	NI	NI

IMPORTANT

The buying prices listed are for notes in **Very Fine (VF)** condition (see page 121).

Note:. NI - Not Issued

MODIFIED PORTRAIT

MODIFIED PORTRAIT

The portrait was modified by darkening the highlights in the hair and thus removing the shading which had resulted in the devil's face. The modification of the face plates was made for most denominations in 1956, except for the $1,000 denomination, which was modified several years later.

	Very Fine Buying Price by Signature							
	Beattie/Coyne		Beattie/Rasminsky		Bouey/Raminsky		Lawson/Bouey	
Denom.	Regular	Asterisk	Regular	Asterisk	Regular	Asterisk	Regular	Asterisk
$1	1.00	5.00	1.00	1.00	1.00	3.00	1.00	3.00
$2	2.00	3.00	2.00	3.00	2.00	3.00	2.00	3.00
$5	5.00	40.00	5.00	8.00	5.00	7.00	NI	NI
$10	10.00	50.00	10.00	12.00	NI	NI	NI	NI
$20	20.00	50.00	20.00	50.00	NI	NI	NI	NI
$50	50.00	NI	50.00	NI	NI	NI	50.00	NI
$100	100.00	NI	100.00	NI	NI	NI	100.00	NI
$1,000	1,025.00	NI	1,025.00	NI	1,025.00	NI	1,025.00	NI

IMPORTANT

The buying prices listed are for notes in **Very Fine (VF)** condition (see page 121).

Note:. NI - Not Issued

$1 CENTENNIAL 1967

For the centennial of Canada's Confederation a special $1 note was issued. The note has a single design and two types of serial numbers, regular serial numbers and a special number "1867 - 1967." The special series was available from the Bank of Canada as a collector's item, but examples were soon found in circulation. In addition, there was an asterisk note series for replacement notes.

Denom.	Issue Date	Variety	Uncirculated Buying Price
$1	1967	Commemorative Serial Number 1867-1967	1.00
$1	1967	Regular Serial Number	1.00
$1	1967	Asterisk Serial Number	10.00

1969 - 1975 ISSUE

This new series combined fine line engraving with subtle variations to make notes that are extremely difficult to counterfeit. The series features a new portrait of the Queen, as well as portraits of previous prime ministers of Canada.

IMPORTANT

The buying prices listed on the following page are for notes in **Uncirculated (Unc)** condition (new). The note must be clean, crisp, with no tears, creases, folds or marks of any kind or description.

1969-1975 ISSUES

ASTERISK AND "X" REPLACEMENT NOTES

Replacement of defective notes by asterisk notes was continued when the 1969-1975 issue was introduced. The highest denomination of the 1954 issue to be printed with asterisks was the $20; however, all denominations in the 1969-1975 issue, including the $50 and $100 notes, occur with asterisks in front of the two-letter prefix type.

When the triple-letter prefix notes were introduced in 1981, the use of the asterisk was discontinued. For triple-letter prefix notes, a replacement note was then designated by the use of an "X" for the third letter.

Asterisk Notes
BC-46aA

"X" Replacement Notes
BC-46A-i

	Uncirculated Buying Price by Signature								
	Beattie/Rasminsky		Bouey/Rasminsky		Lawson/Bouey			Crow/Bouey	
Denom.	Regular	Asterisk	Regular	Asterisk	Regular	Asterisk	X	Regular	X
$1	NI	NI	NI	NI	1.	8.	15.	1.	7.
$2	NI	NI	NI	NI	3.	20.	50.	3.	100.
$5	NI	NI	10.	50.	10.	65.	NI	NI	NI
$10	20.	50.	20.	50.	15.	75.	400.	12.	40.
$20	30.	125.	NI	NI	25.	100.	NI	NI	NI
$50	NI	NI	NI	NI	70.	400.	1,000.	60.	100.
$100	NI	NI	NI	NI	100.	500.	1,000.	100.	150.

IMPORTANT

The buying prices listed are for notes in **Very Fine (VF)** condition (see page 121).

1979 ISSUES

The series beginning in 1979 is a modification of the previous issue. The face designs are similar, as is the colouration. The serial numbers are moved to the back of the note at the bottom, where the name of the Bank of Canada previously appeared. The black serial numbers are machine readable.

IMPORTANT

The buying prices listed below are for notes in uncirculated condition (new). The note must be clean, crisp, with no tears, creases, folds or marks of any kind or description.

REPLACEMENT NOTES

There are no asterisk notes in this issue. The replacement notes are designated by the second digit in the serial number.

The digit 1 following the first digit 3 of the $5 notes designates a replacement note. In the $20 denomination the replacement notes can be distinguished by "510" for the CBN company and "516" for the BABN company.

$5 Replacement Note

$20 Replacement Note

Denom.	Uncirculated Buying Price by Signature					
	Lawson/Bouey		Crow/Bouey		Thiessen/Crow	
	Regular	Replace.	Regular	Replace.	Regular	Replace.
$5	7.00	100.00	7.00	300.00	NI	NI
$20	22.00	300.00	22.00	75.00	20.00	40.00

IMPORTANT

The buying prices listed are for notes in **Uncirculated (Unc)** condition (see page 124).

1986 BIRD ISSUES

On March 14, 1986, the Bank of Canada introduced a new series of bank notes. The new designs were launched that year with the issue of the $2 and $5 notes. The $1 and $2 bank notes have since been replaced with $1 and $2 coins.

$5 Replacement Note

Denom.	Signature	Regular	Replacement
$2	Crow / Bouey	2.00	15.00
$5	Crow / Bouey	10.00	100.00

	Uncirculated Buying Price by Signature							
	Theissen/Crow		Bonin/Theissen		Knight/Thiessen		Knight/Dodge	
Denom.	Regular	Replace.	Regular	Replace.	Regular	Replace.	Regular	Replace.
$2	2.00	3.00	2.00	3.00	NI	NI	NI	NI
$5	5.00	7.00	5.00	60.00	5.00	100.00	5.00	20.00
$10	10.00	30.00	10.00	100.00	10.00	NI	NI	NI
$20	20.00	40.00	20.00	40.00	20.00	100.00	20.00	25.00
$50	50.00	100.00	50.00	NI	50.00	NI	50.00	100.00
$100	100.00	200.00	100.00	NI	100.00	NI	100.00	200.00
$1000	1,000.00	1,250.00	1,000.00	NI	NI	NI	NI	NI

IMPORTANT

The buying prices listed are for notes in **Uncirculated (Unc)** condition (see page 124).

Without Security Device

With Security Device

Without Security Device

With Security Device

Denom.	Uncirculated Buying Price by Signature		
	Knight/Thiessen	Knight/Dodge	Jenkins/Dodge
$5 Without Security Device	NI	5.00	5.00
$5 With Security Device	NI	NI	5.00
$10 Without Security Device	10.00	10.00	10.00
$10 With Security Device	NI	NI	10.00
$20 With Security Device	NI	NI	20.00
$50 With Security Device	NI	NI	50.00
$100 With Security Device	NI	NI	100.00

IMPORTANT

Prices listed are buying prices for notes in **uncirculated (new)** condition.
No identifiable replacement notes have been printed for this issue.

NEWFOUNDLAND
PUBLIC WORKS CASH NOTES

1901-1909

Denom.	Buying Price
40 cents	150.00
50 cents	175.00
80 cents	200.00
$1	150.00
$5	750.00

1910-1911

Denom.	Buying Price
25 cents	85.00
50 cents	90.00
$1	150.00
$2	1,000.00
$5	1,500.00

GOVERNMENT NOTES

Denom.	Buying Price
$1	125.00
$2	150.00

PRINCE EDWARD ISLAND

Denom.	Buying Price
1848-1870 5s	1,000.00
1848-1870 10s	1,000.00
1848-1870 £1	1,000.00
1848-1870 £2	1,000.00
1848-1870 £5	1,000.00
1872 $10	2,000.00
1872 $20	2,000.00

NOVA SCOTIA

Denom.	Buying Price
1846-1854 £1	2,000.00
1861 $5	1,500.00

IMPORTANT

Prices given are for notes in VG or better condition.

CANADIAN COLONIAL TOKENS

Canada has produced a great number of tokens of various kinds over the years. Tokens were used as a form of currency prior to the institution of the decimal currency system in 1858 (Colonial issues are not all tokens, some being regal coins). After Confederation, other kinds of tokens appeared, such as those for services, transportation and advertising purposes.

NEWFOUNDLAND TOKENS

Date and Description	Buying Price
1858 Sailing Ship	250.00
1860 Fishery Rights	30.00

Date and Description	Buying Price
Rutherford - St. John's	4.00
Rutherford - Harbour Grace	4.00
McAuslane	2,000.00

Note: Buying prices quoted are for tokens in very good condition. Holed, bent or badly corroded tokens are worth substantially less.

PRINCE EDWARD ISLAND TOKENS

Date and Description	Buying Price	Date and Description	Buying Price
Holey Dollar Ring*	1,750.00	McCarthy Penny	2,000.00
Holey Dollar Plug*	1,750.00	Sheaf of Wheat	600.00
McCausland Penny	1,000.00	Speed The Plough	3.00

Note: * Forgeries exist and are worth considerably less.

PRINCE EDWARD ISLAND TOKENS

Date and Description	Buying Price	Date and Description	Buying Price
Fisheries & Agriculture	3.00	Fisheries & Agriculture	4.00
Self Government 1855 Prince Edward's	3.00	Ships Colonies 1815 One Penny	15.00
Self Government 1855 Prince Edward	3.00	Ships Colonies 1815 Publick Accommodation	10.00
Self Government 1857	3.00	Ships Colonies	3.50

Note: Tokens must be **VG (very good)** or better condition, with no discolouration or damage.

NOVA SCOTIA SEMI-REGAL TOKENS

Date and Description	Buying Price	Date and Description	Buying Price
1823 Halfpenny	2.00	1840 Halfpenny	2.00
1824 Halfpenny	2.00	1840 Penny	3.00
1824 Penny	4.00	1843 Halfpenny	3.00
1832 Halfpenny	2.00	1843 Penny	4.00
1832 Penny	4.00	1856 Halfpenny	3.00
		1856 Penny	3.00

NOVA SCOTIA TOKENS

Date and Description	Buying Price	Date and Description	Buying Price
Broke - Halifax	5.00	Hosterman & Etter 1815	6.00
Convenience of Trade	20.00	Starr & Shannon	3.00
Carritt & Alport	6.00	Commercial Change	5.00
Hosterman & Etter, 1814	6.00	Miles W. White	6.00

Date and Description	Buying Price	Date and Description	Buying Price
John Alexr Barry	4.00	Trade & Navigation 1813	15.00
Halifax Nova Scotia	10.00	Trade & Navigation 1812 and 1813	4.00
W. A. & S. Black's	10.00	Pure Copper Preferable	3.00
J. Brown	5.00	Success to Navigation	3.00
W. L. White's	20.00	N.S & N.B. Success	15.00

Date and Description	Buying Price
1843 Halfpenny	2.00
1843 Penny	3.00
1854 Halfpenny	2.00
1854 Penny	3.00

Date and Description	Buying Price
McDermott	325.00
St. John	6.00
St. John's	5,000.00

LOWER CANADA TOKENS

Date and Description	Buying Price	Date and Description	Buying Price
Magdalen Island	30.00	Pro Bono Publico	5,000.00
Bank Token	3.00	Bank Token Halfpenny	2.00
Banque du Peuple, Maple Leaf	4.00	Bank Token Penny	3.00
Banque du Peuple, Wreath	2.00	Bank of Montreal, Sideview Halfpenny	500.00
		Bank of Montreal, Sideview Penny	750.00

Date and Description	Buying Price	Date and Description	Buying Price
Montreal Half Penny	3.00	Francis Mullins & Son	5.00
Canada Half Penny, 1841	3.00	R.W. Owen	6,000.00
For Public Accommodation	4.00	J. Shaw & Co.	5.00
T.S. Brown & Co.	3.00	J. Roy	30.00
Ths & Wm Molson	300.00	Agriculture & Commerce	2.00

Date and Description	Buying Price	Date and Description	Buying Price
Halfpenny Token 1812, Small Wreath	3.00	To Facilitate Trade	
Halfpenny Token 1812, Large Wreath	4.00	Military Bust 1825	4.00
Penny Token 1812	4.00	Civilian Bust 1825	800.00
Victoria Nobis Est	4.00	Spread Eagle	3.00
R H Half Penny	5.00	Halfpenny Token	5.00

LOWER CANADA TOKENS

Date and Description	Buying Price	Date and Description	Buying Price
Seated Justice	3.00	Commercial Change	3.00
Bust/Ships Colonies	4.00	Bust and Harp	6.00

WELLINGTON TOKENS

Date and Description	Buying Price	Date and Description	Buying Price
Field Marshal Wellington	3.00	The Illustrious Wellington	3.00
Marquis Wellington	4.00	Battle Token	3.00

Date and Description	Buying Price
Copper Company	500.00
Lesslie Halfpenny	5.00
Lesslie Twopenny	75.00
No Labour No Bread	3.00
Sir Isaac Brock	4.00

Date and Description	Buying Price
Success To Commerce	3.00
Upper & Lower Canada	25.00
Commercial Change 1815	20.00
Commerical Change 1820	3.00

Note: Not all Canadian colonial tokens are listed in this guide. For more detailed information see the Charlton Standard Catalogue of Canadian Colonial Tokens, 7th edition.

UPPER CANADA TOKENS

Date and Description	Buying Price	Date and Description	Buying Price
Commercial Change 1821		To Facilitate Trade	
Cask Marked Upper Canada	25.00	1823	3.00
Cask Marked Jamaica	400.00	1833	1.75
Province of Upper Canada	12.00	Commercial Change 1833	3.00

PROVINCE OF CANADA TOKENS

PROVINCE OF CANADA TOKENS

Date and Description	Buying Price
Bank of Montreal	
1842, 1844 Halfpenny	2.00
1845 Halfpenny	2,500.00
1837 Penny	60.00
1842 Penny	3.00

Date and Description	Buying Price
Quebec Bank, 1852 Halfpenny	2.00
Quebec Bank, 1852 Penny	3.00
Bank of Upper Canada 1850-1857	
Halfpenny	2.00
Penny	3.00

ANONYMOUS AND MISCELLANEOUS TOKENS

Date and Description	Buying Price
For General Accommodation	3.00
Success to Trade	20.00

Date and Description	Buying Price
Pure Copper Preferable	4.00
North American	20.00

BRITISH COLUMBIA TOKENS

Date and Description	Buying Price
1862 Pattern Gold $10	50,000.00
1862 Pattern Gold $20	50,000.00

NORTH WEST COMPANY

Date and Description	Buying Price
1820 North West Company Token	1,000.00

Note: Beware reproductions exist.

HUDSON'S BAY COMPANY

Date and Description	Buying Price
Hudson's Bay Company Tokens Set of four (1, ½, ¼, 1/8)	600.00

TRANSPORTATION TOKENS

Date and Description	Buying Price
Bridge Tokens, each	250.00
Montreal & Lachine Railroad	250.00
Montreal & Lachine Railroad Restrike Dated 1947	50.00

CANADIAN MEDALS

WAR MEDALS 1812 TO 1885

Army
Gold
Cross

Naval
General
Service
Medal

Army
Gold
Medal

Canadian
General
Service
Medal

Army
General
Service
Medal

Egyptian
Medal

Date and Description	Buying Price
Army Gold Cross	16,000.00
Army Gold Medal	6,000.00
Army General Service Medal 1812-1814	
Fort Detroit Bar	2,000.00
Chateauguay Bar	2,000.00
Chrysler's Farm Bar	2,000.00
Naval General Service Medal 1812-1814	200.00

Date and Description	Buying Price
Canadian General Service Medal	
Fenian Raid Bar 1866	150.00
Fenian Raid Bar 1870	150.00
Red River Bar 1870	550.00
Egypt Medal	
The Nile Bar	550.00
Kirbekan Bar	550.00
*Awarded to Canadian Boatmen	

WAR MEDALS 1885 TO 1914

Khedive's
Bronze
Star

1914
Star

North West
Canada
Medal

1914-1915
Star

South
Africa
Medal

British
War
Medal

Date and Description	Buying Price	Date and Description	Buying Price
Khedive's Bronze Star	30.00	1914 Star*	1,000.00
North West Canada Medal 1885	200.00	1914-1915 Star	8.00
Saskatchewan Bar	250.00	British War Medal	12.00
Queen's South Africa		Groups**	
1899-1900 on reverse	2,500.00	Star, British War Medal (2)	30.00
Dates removed	30.00	Star, Allied Victory Medal	35.00
King's South Africa	30.00	British War Medal (3)	

*Canadian Star awarded only to 2nd. Field Hospital.
**Groups to Canadian Veterans, named to same person

WAR MEDALS 1914 TO 1945

Allied
Victory
Medal

Canadian
Defence
Medal

Merchantile
Marine
War
Medal

Canadian
WW II
1939-1945
War
Medal

Canadian
Volunteer
Service
Medal

Atlantic
Air Crew
Europe
Africa
France and
Germany
Italy
Pacific
Burma

Date and Description	Buying Price	Date and Description	Buying Price
Allied Victory Medal	8.00	1939-1945 Star	7.00
Mercantile Marine War Medal	12.00	Atlantic Star	20.00
Canadian Volunteer Service Medal	12.00	Air Crew Europe	60.00
Defence Medal	12.00	Africa Star	7.00
1939-1945 War Medal	12.00	France and Germany Star	7.00
		Italy Star	7.00
		Pacific Star	12.00
		Burma Star	12.00

Note: The Canadian Volunteer Service Medal, the Canadian Defence Medal and the World War II Medal are issued in silver. Britain and other Commonwealth countries issued cupro-nickel medals.

WAR MEDALS
1951 TO 1973

COMMEMORATIVE MEDALS

Canadian
Korean
Medal

1911
Coronation
Medal

United
Nations
Korea
Medal

1935
Silver
Jubilee
Medal

United
Nations
Emergency
Medal

1937
Coronation
Medal

Date and Description	Buying Price
Canadian Korean War Medal, English	30.00
Canadian Korean War Medal, French	40.00
United Nations Korea Medal	17.50
United Nations Emergency Medal	17.50
United Nations Medal 1960 to present	17.50
International Commission Medal 1967	17.50
International Commission Medal 1973	17.50

Date and Description	Buying Price
King George V	
Coronation Medal - 1911	22.00
Silver Jubilee Medal - 1935	17.50
King George VI	
Coronation Medal - 1937	17.50

COMMEMORATIVE MEDALS	MEDALS FOR VALOUR AND SERVICE

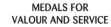

1953 Coronation Medal

Victoria Cross

1977 Silver Jubilee Medal

Distinguished Service Order

1967 Canadian Centennial Medal

Order of St. Michael and St. George

Date and Description	Buying Price
Queen Elizabeth II	
Coronation Medal - 1953	17.50
Silver Jubilee Medal - 1977	40.00
Canadian Centennial Medal - 1967	30.00

Date and Description	Buying Price
Victoria Cross	40,000.00
Awarded to a Canadian	65,000.00
Distinguished Service Order	250.00
Order of St. Michael and St. George	250.00

MEDALS FOR VALOUR AND SERVICE

Distinguished
Service
Cross

Air Force
Medal

Distinguished
Flying
Cross

Military
Medal

Air Force
Cross

British
Empire
Medal

Date and Description	Buying Price	Date and Description	Buying Price
Distinguished Service Cross	300.00	Air Force Medal	175.00
Distinguished Flying Cross	400.00	Military Medal	225.00
Air Force Cross	500.00	British Empire Medal	60.00

150

COINS OF THE UNITED STATES

MINT MARKS

The United States decimal coinage is identified by the following mint marks:

C	-Charlotte, North Carolina
CC	-Carson City, Nevada
D	-Dahlonega, Georgia (gold coins only)
D	-Denver, Colorado (1906 to date)
O	-New Orleans, Louisiana
S	-San Francisco, California
P	-Philadelphia, Pennsylvania

HALF CENTS

Liberty Cap

Date and Mint Mark	Buying Price
1793 Head Facing Left	900.00
1794	175.00
1795	130.00
1796	4,000.00
1797	150.00

Draped Bust

Date and Mint Mark	Buying Price
1800	25.00
1802	400.00
1803-1808	25.00

Classic Head

Date and Mint Mark	Buying Price
1809-1810	15.00
1811	100.00
1825 to 1829	15.00
1831 Proof only	1,000.00
1832 to 1835	14.00

Coronet Head

Date and Mint Mark	Buying Price
1849 to 1851	15.00
1852 Proof only	350.00
1853 to 1856	10.00
1857	15.00

IMPORTANT

Buying prices are for coins in VG condition. Coins in lessor grades such as Good or About Good will command lower buying prices.

LARGE CENTS

Flowing Hair

Date and Mint Mark	Buying Price
1793 Chain Reverse	2,500.00
1793 Wreath Reverse	875.00

Liberty Cap

Date and Mint Mark	Buying Price
1793	1,500.00
1794	100.00
1795	75.00
1796	100.00

Draped Bust

Date and Mint Mark	Buying Price
1796	75.00
1797	45.00
1798	25.00
1799	800.00
1800 to 1803	25.00
1804	250.00
1805 to 1807	20.00

Classic Head

Date and Mint Mark	Buying Price
1808	25.00
1809	50.00
1810	20.00
1811	30.00
1812 to 1814	20.00

Coronet Head

Date and Mint Mark	Buying Price
1816 to 1820	5.00
1821	12.00
1822	7.00
1823	25.00
1824 to 1838	5.00
1839 to 1856	5.00
1857	15.00

SMALL CENTS

Flying Eagle

Date and Mint Mark	Buying Price
1856	3,000.00
1857 to 1858	7.00

Indian Head

Date and Mint Mark	Buying Price
1859	4.00
1860 to 1865	3.00
1866 to 1868	14.00
1869 to 1872	20.00
1873 to 1876	7.00
1877	300.00
1878	9.00
1879 to 1886	.50
1887 to 1908	.25
1908S	20.00
1909	3.50
1909S	150.00

Lincoln Head Wheat Ears

Date and Mint Mark	Buying Price
1909	.50
1909VDB	2.00
1909S	20.00
1909S VDB	200.00
1910 to 1914	.05
1914D	60.00
1915D to 1931D	.02
1931S	30.00
1932 to 1958	.01
1955 Double Die	100.00

Lincoln Head Memorial

Date and Mint Mark	Buying Price
1959 to 2008	.01

TWO CENTS

Date and Mint Mark	Buying Price
1864 to 1871	4.00
1872	100.00
1873 Proofs only	400.00

THREE CENTS

Silver

Date and Mint Mark	Buying Price
1851 to 1862	8.00
1863 to 1872	100.00
1873 Proofs only	200.00

Nickel

Date and Mint Mark	Buying Price
1865 to 1874	4.00
1875 to 1876	7.00
1877 to 1878 Proofs only	200.00
1879 to 1880	18.00
1881	4.00
1882	25.00
1883	40.00
1884 to 1887	120.00
1888	15.00
1889	25.00

HALF DIMES

Flowing Hair

Date and Mint Mark	Buying Price
1794	375.00
1795	300.00

Draped Bust

Date and Mint Mark	Buying Price
1796 to 1797	400.00
1800 to 1801	225.00
1802	6,000.00
1803 to 1805	200.00

Capped Bust

Date and Mint Mark	Buying Price
1829 to 1837	10.00

Liberty Seated

Date and Mint Mark	Buying Price
1837 Large Date	10.00
1837 Small Date	10.00
1838 to 1845	5.00
1838 O	30.00

Date and Mint Mark	Buying Price
1844O	20.00
1846	100.00
1847 to 1862	5.00
1863	50.00
1863S	10.00
1864	100.00
1864S	10.00
1865	50.00
1865S	10.00
1866	50.00
1866S	10.00
1867	150.00
1867S to 1873S	5.00

FIVE CENTS NICKEL

Shield

Date and Mint Mark	Buying Price
1866 to 1870	5.00
1871	15.00
1872 to 1876	8.00
1877 and 1878 Proofs only	200.00
1879 to 1881	100.00
1882 to 1883	5.00

Liberty Head

Date and Mint Mark	Buying Price
1883	2.00
1884	5.00
1885	160.00
1886	75.00
1887 to 1898	2.00
1899 to 1912D	.25
1912S	50.00

Indian Head

Date and Mint Mark	Buying Price
1913 and 1913D	2.00
1913S	15.00
1914D	25.00
1914S	10.00
1914 to 1918	1.00
1918D 8/7	400.00
1919 to 1938	.15

Jefferson Head

Date and Mint Mark	Buying Price
1938 to 1942 Nickel	.05
1942 to 1945 Silver,	
Large P, D, or S above Monticello	.25
1946 to 2010 Nickel	.05

DIMES

Draped Bust

Date and Mint Mark	Buying Price
1796 to 1797	500.00
1798 to 1807	100.00

Capped Bust

Date and Mint Mark	Buying Price
1809 to 1811	40.00
1814 to 1821	8.00
1822	150.00
1823 to 1837	8.00

Liberty Seated

Date and Mint Mark	Buying Price
1837 and 1838O No stars	12.00
1838 to 1840O Stars	5.00
1841 to 1843	5.00
1843O	20.00
1844	100.00
1845 to 1845O	5.00
1846	40.00
1847 to 1856	4.00
1856S	65.00
1857 to 1860	4.00
1858S	40.00
1859S	50.00
1860O	150.00
1861 to 1862	4.00
1863	100.00
1863S	10.00
1864	50.00
1864S	10.00
1865	100.00
1865S	10.00
1866	125.00
1866S	10.00
1867	150.00
1867S	10.00
1868 to 1874	5.00
1871CC	750.00
1872CC	250.00
1873CC Arrows	600.00
1874CC Arrows	1,000.00
1875 to 1878	4.00
1878CC	20.00
1879 to 1881	60.00
1882 to 1885	4.00
1885S	150.00
1886 to 1891	3.50

Barber

Date and Mint Mark	Buying Price
1892 to 1895	4.00
1895O	125.00
1896O and S	40.00
1897 to 1916	.80

Mercury Head

Date and Mint Mark	Buying Price
1916	.80
1916D	500.00
1917 to 1945	.80
1921	22.00
1921D	40.00

Roosevelt - Silver

Date and Mint Mark	Buying Price
1946 to 1964	.80

Roosevelt - Clad

Date and Mint Mark	Buying Price
1965 to 2010	.10

TWENTY CENTS

Date and Mint Mark	Buying Price
1875 to 1876	30.00
1877 to 1878 Proofs only	500.00

QUARTER DOLLAR

Draped Bust

Date and Mint Mark	Buying Price
1796	3,500.00
1804	1,000.00
1805 to 1807	75.00

Capped Bust

Date and Mint Mark	Buying Price
1815 to 1822	25.00
1823/2	4,000.00
1824 to 1828	25.00
1831 to 1838 Reduced Size	20.00

Liberty Seated

Date and Mint Mark	Buying Price
1838 to 1841	7.00
1842 Large Date	20.00
1842O Small Date	100.00
1842O Large date	8.00
1843 to 1849	5.00
1849O	150.00
1850 to 1851	8.00
1851O	60.00
1852	14.00
1852O	60.00
1853 to 1865	6.00
1862S and 1865S	15.00
1864S	75.00
1866 to 1867S	60.00
1868 to 1870	20.00
1870CC and 1871CC	500.00
1871 to 1878CC	7.00
1871S	75.00
1872CC	175.00
1872S	200.00
18773CC	600.00
1878S to 1888	30.00
1888S	5.00
1889 and 1890	15.00
1891 and 1891S	5.00
1891O	40.00

Barber

Date and Mint Mark	Buying Price
1892 to 1896	2.000
1896S	200.00
1897 to 1901	2.00
1901S	2,000.00
1902 to 1913	2.00
1913S	500.00
1914 to 1916D	2.00

Standing Liberty

Date and Mint Mark	Buying Price
1916	1,500.00
1917 to 1924	5.00
1923S	125.00
1925 to 1930	2.00

Washington - Silver

Date and Mint Mark	Buying Price
1932 to 1964	2.00
1927S	10.00
1932D	50.00
1932S	50.00
1933 to 1964	2.00

Washington - Clad

Date and Mint Mark	Buying Price
1965 to 1998	.25

200th Bi-Centennial

Date and Mint Mark	Buying Price
1976	.25

STATE QUARTERS

Delaware	Pennsylvania	Maryland	South Carolina

New Jersey	Georgia	New Hampshire	Virginia

Connecticut	Massachusetts	New York	North Carolina

Date and Mint Mark	Description	Buying Price	Date and Mint Mark	Description	Buying Price
1999P	Delaware, MS	.25	2000P	Maryland, MS	.25
1999D	Delaware, MS	.25	2000D	Maryland, MS	.25
1999S	Delaware, PR	1.25	2000S	Maryland, PR	1.25
1998S	Delaware, Silver	5.00	2000S	Maryland, Silver	2.50
1999P	Pennsylvania, MS	.25	2000P	South Carolina, MS	.25
1999D	Pennsylvania, MS	.25	2000D	South Carolina, MS	.25
1999S	Pennsylvania, PR	1.25	2000S	South Carolina, PR	1.25
1999S	Pennsylvania, Silver	4.00	2000S	South Carolina, Silver	2.50
1999P	New Jersey, MS	.25	2000P	New Hampshire, MS	.25
1999D	New Jersey, MS	.25	2000D	New Hampshire, MS	.25
1999S	New Jersey, PR	1.25	2000S	New Hampshire, PR	1.25
1999S	New Jersey, Silver	4.00	2000S	New Hampshire, Silver	2.50
1999P	Georgia, MS	.25	2000P	Virginia, MS	.25
1999D	Georgia, MS	.25	2000D	Virginia, MS	.25
1999S	Georgia, PR	1.25	2000S	Virginia, PR	1.25
1999S	Georgia, Silver	4.00	2000S	Virginia, Silver	2.50
1999P	Connecticut, MS	.25	2001P	New York, MS	.25
1999D	Connecticut, MS	.25	2001D	New York, MS	.25
1999S	Connecticut, PR	1.25	2001S	New York, PR	1.25
1999S	Connecticut, Silver	5.00	2001S	New York, Silver	2.50
2000P	Massachusetts, MS	.25	2001P	North Carolina, MS	.25
2000D	Massachusetts, MS	.25	2001D	North Carolina, MS	.25
2000S	Massachusetts, PR	1.25	2001S	North Carolina, PR	1.25
2000S	Massachusetts, Silver	2.50	2001S	North Carolina, Silver	2.50

STATE QUARTERS (cont.)

Rhode Island   Vermont   Indiana   Mississippi

Kentucky   Tennessee   Illinois   Alabama

Ohio   Louisiana   Maine   Missouri

Date and Mint Mark	Description	Buying Price	Date and Mint Mark	Description	Buying Price
2001P	Rhode Island, MS	.25	2002P	Indiana, MS	.25
2001D	Rhode Island, MS	.25	2002D	Indiana, MS	.25
2001S	Rhode Island, PR	1.25	2002S	Indiana, PR	1.25
2001S	Rhode Island, Silver	2.50	2002S	Indiana, Silver	2.50
2001P	Vermont, MS	.25	2002P	Mississippi, MS	.25
2001D	Vermont, MS	.25	2002D	Mississippi, MS	.25
2001S	Vermont, PR	1.25	2002S	Mississippi, PR	1.25
2001S	Vermont, Silver	2.50	2002S	Mississippi, Silver	2.50
2001P	Kentucky, MS	.25	2003P	Illinois, MS	.25
2001D	Kentucky, MS	.25	2003D	Illinois, MS	.25
2001S	Kentucky, PR	1.25	2003S	Illinois, PR	1.25
2001S	Kentucky, Silver	2.50	2003S	Illinois, Silver	2.50
2002P	Tennessee, MS	.25	2003P	Alabama, MS	.25
2002D	Tennessee, MS	.25	2003D	Alabama, MS	.25
2002S	Tennessee, PR	1.25	2003S	Alabama, PR	1.25
2002S	Tennessee, Silver	2.50	2003S	Alabama, Silver	2.50
2002P	Ohio, MS	.25	2003P	Maine, MS	.25
2002D	Ohio, MS	.25	2003D	Maine, MS	.25
2002S	Ohio, PR	1.25	2003S	Maine, PR	1.25
2002S	Ohio, Silver	2.50	2003S	Maine, Silver	2.50
2002P	Louisiana, MS	.25	2003P	Missouri, MS	.25
2002D	Louisiana, MS	.25	2003D	Missouri, MS	.25
2002S	Louisiana, PR	1.25	2003S	Missouri, PR	1.25
2002S	Louisiana, Silver	2.50	2003S	Missouri, Silver	2.50

STATE QUARTERS (cont.)

Arkansas	Michigan	California	Minnesota
Florida	Texas	Oregon	Kansas
Iowa	Wisconsin	West Virginia	Nevada

Date and Mint Mark	Description	Buying Price	Date and Mint Mark	Description	Buying Price
2003P	Arkansas, MS	.25	2005P	California, MS	.25
2003D	Arkansas, MS	.25	2005D	California, MS	.25
2003S	Arkansas, PR	1.25	2005S	California, PR	1.25
2003S	Arkansas, Silver	2.50	2005S	California, Silver	2.50
2004P	Michigan, MS	.25	2005P	Minnesota, MS	.25
2004D	Michigan, MS	.25	2005D	Minnesota, MS	.25
2004S	Michigan, PR	1.25	2005S	Minnesota, PR	1.25
2004S	Michigan, Silver	2.50	2005S	Minnesota, Silver	2.50
2004P	Florida, MS	.25	2005P	Oregon, MS	.25
2004D	Florida, MS	.25	2005D	Oregon, MS	.25
2004S	Florida, PR	1.25	2005S	Oregon, PR	1.25
2004S	Florida, Silver	2.50	2005S	Oregon, Silver	2.50
2004P	Texas, MS	.25	2005P	Kansas, MS	.25
2004D	Texas, MS	.25	2005D	Kansas, MS	.25
2004S	Texas, PR	1.25	2005S	Kansas, PR	1.25
2004S	Texas, Silver	2.50	2005S	Kansas, Silver	2.50
2004P	Iowa, MS	.25	2005P	West Virginia, MS	.25
2004D	Iowa, MS	.25	2005D	West Virginia, MS	.25
2004S	Iowa, PR	1.25	2005S	West Virginia, PR	1.25
2004S	Iowa, Silver	2.50	2005S	West Virginia, Silver	2.50
2004P	Wisconsin, MS	.25	2006P	Nevada, MS	.25
2004D	Wisconsin, MS	.25	2006D	Nevada, MS	.25
2004S	Wisconsin, PR	1.25	2006S	Nevada, PR	2.00
2004S	Wisconsin, Silver	2.50	2006S	Nevada, Silver	2.50

STATE QUARTERS (cont.)

Nebraska	Colorado	Idaho	Wyoming
North Dakota	South Dakota	Utah	Oklahoma
Montana	Washington	New Mexico	Arizona

Date and Mint Mark	Description	Buying Price	Date and Mint Mark	Description	Buying Price
2006P	Nebraska, MS	.25	2007P	Idaho, MS	.25
2006D	Nebraska, MS	.25	2007D	Idaho, MS	.25
2006S	Nebraska, PR	1.25	2007S	Idaho, PR	1.25
2006S	Nebraska, Silver	2.50	2007S	Idaho, Silver	2.50
2006P	Colorado, MS	.25	2007P	Wyoming, MS	.25
2006D	Colorado, MS	.25	2007D	Wyoming, MS	.25
2006S	Colorado, PR	1.25	2007S	Wyoming, PR	1.25
2006S	Colorado, Silver	2.50	2007S	Wyoming, Silver	2.50
2006P	North Dakota, MS	.25	2007P	Utah, MS	.25
2006D	North Dakota, MS	.25	2007D	Utah, MS	.25
2006S	North Dakota, PR	1.25	2007S	Utah, PR	1.25
2006S	North Dakota, Silver	2.50	2007S	Utah, Silver	2.50
2006P	South Dakota, MS	.25	2008P	Oklahoma, MS	.25
2006D	South Dakota, MS	.25	2008D	Oklahoma, MS	.25
2006S	South Dakota, PR	1.25	2008S	Oklahoma, PR	1.25
2006S	South Dakota, Silver	2.50	2008S	Oklahoma, Silver	2.50
2007P	Montana, MS	.25	2008P	New Mexico, MS	.25
2007D	Montana, MS	.25	2008D	New Mexico, MS	.25
2007S	Montana, PR	1.25	2008S	New Mexico, PR	1.25
2007S	Montana, Silver	2.50	2008S	New Mexico, Silver	2.50
2007P	Washington, MS	.25	2008P	Arizona, MS	.25
2007D	Washington, MS	.25	2008D	Arizona, MS	.25
2007S	Washington, PR	1.25	2008S	Arizona, PR	1.25
2007S	Washington, Silver	2.50	2008S	Arizona, Silver	2.50

STATE QUARTERS (cont.)

Alaska

Hawaii

District of Columbia

Puerto Rico

Guam

American Samoa

U.S. Virgin Islands

Northern Mariana Islands

Date and Mint Mark	Description	Buying Price
2008P	Alaska, MS	.25
2008D	Alaska, MS	.25
2008S	Alaska, PR	1.25
2008S	Alaska, Silver	2.50
2008P	Hawaii, MS	.25
2008D	Hawaii, MS	.25
2008S	Hawaii, PR	1.25
2008S	Hawaii, Silver	2.50
2009P	District of Columbia, MS	.25
2009D	District of Columbia, MS	.25
2009S	District of Columbia, PR	1.25
2009S	District of Columbia, Silver	2.50
2009P	Puerto Rico, MS	.25
2009D	Puerto Rico, MS	.25
2009S	Puerto Rico, PR	1.25
2009S	Puerto Rico, Silver	2.50

Date and Mint Mark	Description	Buying Price
2009P	Guam, MS	.25
2009D	Guam, MS	.25
2009S	Guam, PR	1.25
2009S	Guam, Silver	2.50
2009P	American Samoa, MS	.25
2009D	American Samoa, MS	.25
2009S	American Samoa, PR	1.25
2009S	American Samoa, Silver	2.50
2009P	U.S. Virgin Islands, MS	.25
2009D	U.S. Virgin Islands, MS	.25
2009S	U.S. Virgin Islands, PR	1.25
2009S	U.S. Virgin Islands, Silver	2.50
2009P	Northern Mariana Islands, MS	.25
2009D	Northern Mariana Islands, MS	.25
2009S	Northern Mariana Islands, PR	1.25
2009S	Northern Mariana Islands, Silver	2.50

Note: **MS** is **Mint State**, uncirculated business strike.
PR is **Proof Condition**, collector coins of high quality mirror finish.
Silver Proofs are .900 fine silver coins with a high quality mirror finish.

HALF DOLLARS
Flowing Hair

Date and Mint Mark	Buying Price
1794	1,000.00
1795	250.00

Draped Bust

Date and Mint Mark	Buying Price
1796 15 Stars	6,000.00
1796 16 Stars	6,000.00
1797 15 Stars	6,000.00
1801 to 1802	200.00
1803 to 1807	50.00

Capped Bust

Date and Mint Mark	Buying Price
1807	35.00
1808 to 1814	20.00
1815	350.00

Date and Mint Mark	Buying Price
1817 to 1836	20.00
1837 to 1839	20.00
1839O	50.00

Liberty Seated

Date and Mint Mark	Buying Price
1839 to 1852O	7.00
1850	50.00
1851	50.00
1852	90.00
1853O No Arrows	25,000.00
1853 to 1855	7.00
1855S Arrows	90.00
1856 to 1865S	6.00
1866 to 1873CC	6.00
1870CC	250.00
1871CC	50.00
1873 to 1874S	5.00
1875 to 1878	5.00
1878CC	100.00
1878S	5,000.00
1879 to 1890	50.00
1891	15.00

Barber

Date and Mint Mark	Buying Price
1892	6.00
1892O	75.00
1892S	60.00
1893 to 1897	4.25
1893S	50.00
1897O	50.00
1897S	35.00
1898 to 1915	4.00

Liberty Walking

Date and Mint Mark	Buying Price
1916 to 1920	4.00
1921	60.00
1921D	100.00
1923 to 1947	4.00

Franklin

Date and Mint Mark	Buying Price
1948 to 1964	4.00

Kennedy - Silver

Date and Mint Mark	Buying Price
1964	4.00

Kennedy - Silver Clad

Date and Mint Mark	Buying Price
1965 to 1970	2.50

Kennedy - Copper Clad

Date and Mint Mark	Buying Price
1971 to 2008	.50

SILVER DOLLARS

Flowing Hair

Date and Mint Mark	Buying Price
1794	15,000.00
1795	500.00

Draped Bust

Date and Mint Mark	Buying Price
1795	500.00
1796 to 1798	450.00
1798 to 1803	275.00

Note: Silver dollars must grade very good (VG) or better to command prices listed.

Liberty Seated

Date and Mint Mark	Buying Price
1840 to 1873	75.00
1851 and 1852	1,500.00
1854	450.00
1855	300.00
1858 Proofs only	1,000.00
1870CC	125.00
1870S	20,000.00
1871CC	1,000.00
1872CC	400.00
1872S	100.00
1873CC	1,300.00

Liberty Head

Date and Mint Mark	Buying Price
1878 to 1892	10.00
1878CC to 1881CC	35.00
1882CC to 1884CC	30.00
1885CC	125.00
1889CC	350.00
1893CC	100.00
1890O to 1893O	10.00
1893S	1,100.00
1894	450.00
1895	6,500.00
1895O	100.00
1895S	150.00
1896 to 1903	10.00
1903O	100.00
1904 to 1921	10.00

Peace

Date and Mint Mark	Buying Price
1921	10.00
1922 to 1927	10.00
1928	125.00
1928S to 1935S	10.00

Eisenhower

Date and Mint Mark	Buying Price
1971 to 1978	1.00

Susan B. Anthony

Date and Mint Mark	Buying Price
1979 P.D & S	1.00
1980 P.D & S	1.00
1981 P.D & S	1.00
1999 P & D	1.00

TRADE DOLLARS

Date and Mint Mark	Buying Price
1873 to 1878	30.00
1878CC	100.00
1879 to 1883	300.00

GOLD DOLLARS

Type 1 Liberty Head

Date and Mint Mark	Buying Price
1849 to 1854	70.00
1849C	350.00
1849D	450.00
1850C	350.00
1850D	450.00
1851C	400.00
1851D	425.00
1852C	350.00
1852D	475.00

Type 2 Indian Head, Small

Date and Mint Mark	Buying Price
1854 to 1855	125.00
1855C	450.00
1855D	1,600.00
1855O	165.00
1856S	300.00

GOLD DOLLARS
Type 3 Indian Head, Large

Date and Mint Mark	Buying Price
1856 to 1889	75.00
1856D	1,100.00
1860D	840.00
1861D	2,000.00
1875	700.00

GOLD 2 ½ DOLLARS

Capped Bust Right

Date and Mint Mark	Buying Price
1796	6,000.00
1797 to 1807	1,500.00

Capped Bust Left

Date and Mint Mark	Buying Price
1808	6,000.00

Capped Head Left

Date and Mint Mark	Buying Price
1821 to 1827	1,500.00
1829 to 1833	1,700.00
1834 No Motto	3,000.00

Classic Head

Date and Mint Mark	Buying Price
1834 to 1839	150.00

Coronet Head

Date and Mint Mark	Buying Price
1840 to 1907	125.00
1848 California	6,000.00
1854D	1,000.00
1854S	15,000.00
1855D	1,000.00
1856D	2,500.00
1875	1,500.00

Indian Head

Date and Mint Mark	Buying Price
1908 to 1929	125.00
1911D	900.00

GOLD 3 DOLLARS

Date and Mint Mark	Buying Price
1854 to 1873	350.00
1854D	4,000.00
1873 Closed 3	1,400.00
1880 to 1889	300.00

GOLD 4 DOLLARS

Date and Mint Mark	Buying Price
1879 to 1880	25,000.00

GOLD 5 DOLLARS

Capped Bust - Small Eagle

Date and Mint Mark	Buying Price
1795 to 1797	4,500.00
1798	20,000.00

Capped Bust - Heraldic Eagle

Date and Mint Mark	Buying Price
1795 to 1797	2,000.00
1798 to 1807	1,000.00

IMPORTANT: Buying prices listed are for gold coins graded VF or better. Bent, damaged or badly worn coins are worth bullion value.

Capped Draped Bust Left

Date and Mint Mark	Buying Price
1807 to 1812	1,000.00

Capped Head

Date and Mint Mark	Buying Price
1813 to 1820	1,500.00
1815	20,000.00
1819	3,000.00
1821	3,000.00
1823	1,500.00
1824 to 1826	2,000.00
1829	8,000.00
1830 to 1834	5,000.00

Classic Head

Date and Mint Mark	Buying Price
1834 to 1838	250.00
1838C	1,000.00
1838D	1,000.00

Coronet Head

Date and Mint Mark	Buying Price
1839 to 1908	250.00
1842C Large Date	300.00
1842C Small Date	1,500.00
1854S	35,000.00
1861C	600.00
1861D	1,500.00
1864S	1,600.00
1865S	400.00
1866S	500.00
1870CC	1,800.00
1875	8,000.00
1878CC	850.00

Indian Head

Date and Mint Mark	Buying Price
1908 to 1916	250.00
1909O	750.00
1929	2,000.00

GOLD 10 DOLLARS
Capped Bust Right

Date and Mint Mark	Buying Price
Small Eagle, 1795 to 1797	6,000.00
Heraldic Eagle, 1797 to 1804	2,250.00

Coronet Head

Date and Mint Mark	Buying Price
1838 to 1907S	500.00
1858	1,500.00
1859O	1,500.00
1859S	650.00
1863	1,200.00
1864S	1,500.00
1865S	1,000.00
1866S	550.00
1867S	600.00
1870CC	2,500.00
1871CC	650.00
1872	750.00
1872CC	700.00
1873	1,500.00
1873CC	1,100.00
1875	15,000.00
1875CC	1,100.00
1876	950.00
1876CC	1,000.00
1877	750.00
1877CC	750.00
1878CC	1,000.00
1879CC	1,750.00
1879O	600.00
1883O	800.00

$10 Indian Head

Date and Mint Mark	Buying Price
1907 to 1932	500.00
1920S	2,500.00
1930S	2,000.00
1933	20,000.00

GOLD $20 DOLLARS
Liberty

Date and Mint Mark	Buying Price
1850 to 1907S	1,000.00
1854O	20,000.00
1855O	1,050.00
1856O	25,000.00
1859O	1,250.00
1860O	1,100.00
1861O	1,100.00
1866S	1,000.00
1870CC	35,000.00
1871CC	1,500.00
1872CC	1,000.00
1879O	2,000.00
1881	1,500.00
1882	2,250.00
1885	1,850.00
1886	2,500.00
1891	1,200.00
1891CC	1,200.00

$20 St. Gaudens

Date and Mint Mark	Buying Price
1907 MCMVII	3,000.00
1907 to 1916	1,000.00
1920S	4,500.00
1921	6,000.00
1922 to 1928	1,000.00
1927D	50,000.00
1927S	1,500.00
1929	2,000.00
1930 to 1932	3,000.00

GOLD COMMEMORATIVE COINS

Date and Mint Mark	Buying Price	Date and Mint Mark	Buying Price
1903 $1 Louisiana Purchase	275.00	1995W $5 Civil War	350.00
1904-05 $1 Lewis & Clark Exposition	400.00	1995W $5 WWII	250.00
1915S $1 Panama-Pacific Exposition	275.00	1995W $5 Olympic Torch (MS)	400.00
1916 $1 McKinley Memorial	275.00	1195W $5 Olympic Torch (PR)	250.00
1917 $1 McKinley Memorial	325.00	1995W $5 Olympic Stadium (MS)	500.00
1922 $1 Grant Memorial, With Star	700.00	1995W $5 Olympic Stadium (PR)	300.00
1922 $1 Grant Memorial, Without Star	700.00	1996W $5 Olympic Flag Bearer (MS)	400.00
1915S $2.50 Panama-Pacific Exposition	750.00	1996W $5 Olympic Flag Bearer (PR)	250.00
1926 $2.50 Philadelphia Sesquicentennial	175.00	1996W $5 Olympic Cauldron (MS)	400.00
1984P and D $10 Olympic	500.00	1996W $5 Olympic Cauldron (PR)	250.00
1984S $10 Olympic	500.00	1996W $5 Smithsonian	400.00
1984W $10 Olympic	500.00	1997W $5 F.D.R.	300.00
1986W $5 Liberty	250.00	1997W $5 Jackie Robinson	600.00
1987W $5 Constitution	250.00	1999W $5 George Washington	300.00
1988W $5 Oylmpic	250.00	2000W $10 Library of Congress	700.00
1989W $5 Congress	250.00	2001W $5 Capitol Visitor Centre	300.00
1991W $5 Mount Rushmore	250.00	2002W $5 Salt Lake City Olympics	300.00
1992W $5 Olympic	250.00	2003W $10 First Flight	500.00
1992W $5 Columbus	250.00	2006S $5 San Francisco Mint Museum	250.00
1993W $5 Bill of Rights	250.00	2007W $5 Jamestown	250.00
1994W $5 World Cup	250.00	2008W $5 Bald Eagle	250.00

SILVER COMMEMORATIVE COINS

Date and Mint Mark	Buying Price	Date and Mint Mark	Buying Price
1982D or S 50¢ George Washington	3.00	1996S 50¢ Olympics, Soccer (MS)	60.00
1983P, D or S $1 Los Angeles Olympics	10.00	1996S 50¢ Olympics, Soccer (PR)	35.00
1984P, D or S, $1 Los Angeles Olympics	10.00	1996S 50¢ Olympics, Swimming (MS)	65.00
1986D or S 50¢ Statue of Liberty	3.00	1996S 50¢ Olympics, Swimming (PR)	15.00
1986P or S $1 Statue of Liberty	10.00	1996D $1 Olympics, High Jump (MS)	175.00
1987P or S $1 Constitution	8.00	1996P $1 Olympics, High Jump (PR)	20.00
1988D or S $1 Seoul Olympiad	8.00	1996D $1 Paralympics (MS)	150.00
1989D or S 50¢ Congress	3.00	1996P $1 Paralympics (PR)	35.00
1989D or S $1 Congress	8.00	1996D $1 Olympics, Rowing (MS)	150.00
1990W or P $1 Eisenhower	8.00	1996P $1 Olympics, Rowing (PR)	20.00
1991D or P $1 Korean War	8.00	1996D $1 Olympics, Tennis (MS)	150.00
1991D or S 50¢ Mount Rushmore	7.00	1996P $1 Olympics, Tennis (PR)	35.00
1991D or S $1 USO	8.00	1996D $1 Smithsonian (MS)	65.00
1991P or S $1 Mount Rushmore	12.00	1996P $1 Smithsonian (PR)	15.00
1992D or W $1 White House	12.00	1996S $1 Community Service (MS)	100.00
1992D or S $1 XXV Olympiad	10.00	1996S $1 Community Service (PR)	35.00
1992P or S 50¢ XXV Olympiad	4.00	1997P $1 Botanic Gardens (MS & PR)	15.00
1992D or S 50¢ Christopher Columbus	5.00	1997P $1 Law Enforcement (MS & PR)	60.00
1992D or P $1 Christopher Columbus	12.00	1997S $1 Robinson (MS & PR)	40.00
1993D or W $1 D-Day	15.00	1998S $1 Black Patriots (MS & PR)	50.00
1993-1994P or S $1 Thomas Jefferson	10.00	1998S $1 Robert F. Kennedy (MS & PR)	15.00
1993W or S 50¢ Bill of Rights	7.00	1999P $1 Dolly Madison (MS & PR)	20.00
1993W or S $1 Bill of Rights	10.00	1999P $1 Yellowstone (MS & PR)	20.00
1994D or P 50¢ World Cup	4.00	2000P $1 Leif Ericson (MS & PR)	40.00
1994D or S $1 World Cup	10.00	2000P $1 Library of Congress (MS & PR)	20.00
1994D or S $1 U.S. Capitol	10.00	2001P or D $1 American Indian	150.00
1994W or P $1 Vietnam Veterans Mem.	45.00	2001P 50¢ U.S. Capitol (MS & PR)	5.00
1994W or P $1 U.S. Prisoner of War Museum	50.00	2002P $1 Olympics, Salt Lake City (MS & PR)	15.00
1994W or P $1 Women in Military	20.00	2002W $1 West Point	10.00
1995P 50¢ 50th Anniversary WWII	10.00	2003P 50¢ First Flight (MS & PR)	5.00
1995S 50¢ Civil War Battlefields	20.00	2003P $1 First Flight (MS & PR)	15.00
1995P or S $1 Civil War Battlefields	25.00	2004P $1 Edison (MS & PR)	15.00
1995S 50¢ Olympics, Baseball (MS)	7.00	2004P $1 Lewis & Clark (MS & PR)	15.00
1995S 50¢ Olympics, Baseball (PR)	7.00	2005P $1 Chief Justice J. Marshall (MS & PR)	15.00
1995S 50¢ Olympics, Basketball (MS)	7.00	2005P $1 U.S. Marine Corps (MS & PR)	20.00
1995S 50¢ Olympics, Basketball (PR)	7.00	2006P $1 Benjamin Franklin, Signature	20.00
1995D $1 Olympics, Cycling (MS)	60.00	2006P $1 Benjamin Franklin, Kite	20.00
1995P $1 Olympics, Cycling (PR)	20.00	2006S $1 San Francisco Mint Museum	15.00
1995D $1 Olympics, Gymnastics (MS)	25.00	2007P $1 Jamestown, 400th (MS & PR)	15.00
1995P $1 Olympics, Gymnastics (PR)	15.00	2007P $1 Little Rock High School	15.00
1995D $1 Paralympics (MS)	30.00	2008S $1 Bald Eagle (MS & PR)	10.00
1995S $1 Paralympics (PR)	20.00	2008S 50¢ Bald Eagle (MS & PR)	4.00
1995 W or P $1 Special Olympics	12.00	2009P $1 Louis Braille (MS & PR)	15.00
1995D $1 Olympics, Track & Field (MS)	30.00	2009P $1 Lincoln (MS & PR)	15.00
1995P $1 Olympics, Track & Field (PR)	20.00	2010W $1 Veterans (MS & PR)	15.00
		2010P $1 100th Anniv. Scouts (MS & PR)	15.00

Note: (MS) Mint State
(PR) Proof. Coin has mirror finish.

WORLD GOLD COINS

This partial listing of common world gold coins indicates the prices dealers are willing to pay based on the Canadian dollar gold price as at June 11th, 2010 ($1,227.50 U.S., 1.03 Can./U.S.). Prices will fluctuate with the market price of gold, and the Canadian U.S. dollar exchange rate.

AUSTRIA

Date and Denom.	Fine Gold Content Oz.	Buying Price
1912 10K	0.0980	98.00
1915 20K	0.1960	196.00
1915 100K	0.9803	980.00
1915 1D	0.1109	111.00
1914 4D	0.4438	444.00
1892 10Fr	0.0933	93.00
1892 20Fr*	0.1867	187.00

BAHAMAS

Date and Denom.	Fine Gold Content Oz.	Buying Price
1967 $10	0.1177	118.00
1971 $10	0.1177	118.00
1972 $10	0.0940	94.00
1967 $20	0.2355	236.00
1971 $20*	0.2355	236.00
1972 $20	0.1880	188.00
1967 $50	0.5888	589.00
1971 $50	0.5888	589.00
1972 $50	0.4708	471.00
1967 $100	1.1776	1,178.00
1971 $100	1.1776	1,178.00
1972 $100	0.9420	942.00

BELGIUM

Date and Denom.	Fine Gold Content Oz.	Buying Price
1867 to 1914 20Fr	0.1867	187.00

BERMUDA

Date and Denom.	Fine Gold Content Oz.	Buying Price
1970 $20	0.2355	236.00
1977 $50	0.1172	117.00
1975 $100*	0.2304	230.00
1977 $100	0.2344	234.00

CAYMAN ISLANDS

Date and Denom.	Fine Gold Content Oz.	Buying Price
1972 $25*	0.2532	253.00
1974 $50	0.1823	182.00
1974 $100	0.3646	365.00
1975 $100	0.3646	365.00
1977 $100	0.3646	365.00

* Coin illustrated

CHILE

Date and Denom.	Fine Gold Content Oz.	Buying Price
1898 to 1900 5p	0.0883	88.00
1896 to 1901 10p*	0.1766	177.00
1896 to 1917 20p	0.3532	353.00
1926 to 1980 100p	0.5886	589.00

COLOMBIA

Date and Denom.	Fine Gold Content Oz.	Buying Price
1913 to 1929 2 ½ p	0.1177	118.00
1913 to 1930 5p	0.2355	236.00
1919 and 1924 10p	0.4710	471.00
1973 1500p*	0.5527	553.00

FRANCE

Date and Denom.	Fine Gold Content Oz.	Buying Price
1856 to 1869 5Fr	0.0467	47.00
1854 to 1914 10Fr	0.0933	93.00
1809 to 1914 20Fr*	0.1867	187.00
1810 to 1838 40Fr	0.3734	373.00
1855 to 1864 50Fr	0.4667	467.00
1855 to 1913 100Fr	0.9335	934.00

* Coin illustrated

GERMANY

Date and Denom.	Fine Gold Content Oz.	Buying Price
1872 to 1914 10DM	0.1152	115.00
1871 to 1914 20DM*	0.2304	230.00

GREAT BRITAIN

Date and Denom.	Fine Gold Content Oz.	Buying Price
1863 to 1915 ½ Sov.	0.1177	118.00
1871 to 1968 Sov.*	0.2354	235.00
1887 Two Pound	0.4708	471.00
1897 Two Pound	0.4708	471.00
1902 Two Pound	0.4708	471.00
1911 Two Pound	0.4708	471.00
1937 Two Pound	0.4708	471.00
1887 Five Pound	1.1773	1,177.00
1897 Five Pound	1.1773	1,177.00
1902 Five Pound	1.1773	1,177.00
1911 Five Pound	1.1773	1,177.00
1937 Five Pound	1.1773	1,177.00

IRAN

Date and Denom.	Fine Gold Content Oz.	Buying Price
1971 500R	0.1883	188.00
1971 750R*	0.2827	283.00
1971 1000R	0.3770	377.00
1971 2000R	0.7541	754.00

ITALY

Date and Denom.	Fine Gold Content Oz.	Buying Price
1932 to 1860 10L	0.0931	93.00
1831 to 1860 20L*	0.1867	187.00
1822 to 1831 40L	0.3733	373.00
1832 to 1844 100L	0.9332	933.00

JAMAICA

Date and Denom.	Fine Gold Content Oz.	Buying Price
1972 $20*	0.2531	253.00
1975, 1976 $100	0.2265	227.00
1978 $100	0.3281	328.00
1978, 1979 $250	1.2507	1,251.00

MEXICO

Date and Denom.	Fine Gold Content Oz.	Buying Price
1945 2p	0.0482	48.00
1945 2 1/2p	0.0602	60.00
1955 5p	0.1205	121.00
1959 10p*	0.2411	241.00
1959 20p	0.4823	482.00
1947 50p	1.2057	1,206.00

Above dates are restrikes.

NETHERLANDS

Date and Denom.	Fine Gold Content Oz.	Buying Price
1900 to 1937 1D*	0.1109	111.00
1912 5G	0.0973	97.00
1875 to 1933 10G	0.1947	195.00

PANAMA

Date and Denom.	Fine Gold Content Oz.	Buying Price
1975 to 1979 100B*	0.2361	236.00
1975 to 1979 500B	1.2067	1,208.00

RUSSIA

Date and Denom.	Fine Gold Content Oz.	Buying Price
1897 to 1911 5R*	0.1244	124.00
1897 7 1/2R	0.1867	187.00
1898 to 1911 10R	0.2489	249.00
1897 15R	0.3734	373.00
1977 to 1988 100R	0.5000	500.00

*Coin Illustrated

IMPORTANT: Buying prices listed are for coins graded VF or better. Bent, damaged or badly worn coins may be worth less.

GOLD CONTENT OF CANADIAN GOLD COIN

Denom.	Date and Mint Mark	Gross Weight (Grams)	Fineness	Pure Gold Content Grams	Troy Oz.
1 pd.	1908C-1910C	7.99	.917	7.32	.236
1 pd.	1911C-1919C	7.99	.917	7.32	.236
$2	1865-1888	3.33	.917	3.05	.100
$5	1912-1914	8.36	.900	7.52	.242
$10	1912-1914	16.72	.900	15.05	.484
$20	1967	18.27	.900	16.45	.529
$5 M.L.	1982 to date	3.11	.9999	3.11	.100
$10 M.L.	1982 to date	7.78	.9999	7.78	.250
$20 M.L.	1986 to date	15.57	.9999	15.57	.500
$50 M.L.	1979 to date	31.10	.999	31.10	1.000
$100	1976 (Unc.)	13.33	.583	7.78	.250
$100	1976 (Proof)	16.96	.917	15.55	.499
$100	1977-1986	16.96	.917	15.55	.499
$100	1987 to 2003	13.33	.583	7.78	.250
$100	2004 to date	12.00	.583	7.00	.225
$150	2000 to date	11.84	.750	8.88	.285
$175	1992	16.97	.916	15.544	.500
$200	1990 to 2003	17.106	.916	15.669	.500
$200	2004 to date	16.00	.917	14.67	.472
$250	2006	45.00	.583	26.235	.843
$300 Small	2005 to 2008	45.00	.583	26.235	.843
$300 Large	2002 to 2009	60.00	.583	34.980	1.125
$350 Thick	1998 to 2003	38.05	.99999	38.05	1.223
$350 Thin	2004 to 2009	35.00	.99999	35.00	1.125
$500	2007 to 2009	155.76	.9999	155.76	5.008
$2,500	2007 to 2009	1000.00	.9999	1000.00	32.151

PALLADIUM CONTENT OF CANADIAN PALLADIUM COINS

Denom.	Date	Gross Weight (Grams)	Fineness	Platinum Content Grams	Troy Oz.
$50	2006	31.16	.9995	31.16	1.000

PLATINUM CONTENT OF CANADIAN PLATINUM COINS

Denom.	Date	Gross Weight (Grams)	Fineness	Platinum Content Grams	Troy Oz.
$30	1990-2004	3.12	.9995	3.12	.100
$75	1990-2004	7.79	.9995	7.79	.250
$150	1990-2004	15.58	.9995	15.58	.500
$300	1990-2004	31.13	.9995	31.16	1.000

SILVER CONTENT OF CANADIAN SILVER COINS

Denom.	Date	Gross Weight Grams	Fineness	Silver Content Grams	Troy Oz.
3-cents	2001	5.35	.925	4.95	.159
5-cents	1858-1919, 1998	1.16	.925	1.080	.034
5-cents	1920-1921	1.16	.800	.933	.030
5-cents	1996 to date	5.35	.925	4.95	.159
10-cents	1858-1919	2.33	.925	2.146	.069
10-cents	1920-1967	2.33	.800	1.866	.060
10-cents	1967-1968	2.33	.500	1.170	.038
10-cents	1996 to date	2.40	.925	2.22	.071
25-cents	1870-1919	5.81	.925	5.370	.173
25-cents	1920-1967	5.83	.800	4.665	.150
25-cents	1967-1968	5.83	.500	2.923	.094
25-cents	1996 to date	5.90	.925	5.550	.180
25-cents	1998 (90th)	5.81	.925	5.37	.173
50-cents	1870-1919	11.66	.925	10.792	.347
50-cents	1920-1967, 2003, 2005-2007	11.66	.800	9.330	.300
50-cents	2008 (Train)	20.00	.925	18.50	.595
$1	1935-1967	23.30	.800	18.661	.600
$1	1971-1991	23.20	.500	11.662	.375
$1	1992-2002	25.18	.925	23.29	.750
$1	2003-2004	25.18	.9999	25.18	.810
$1	2005 to date	25.18	.925	23.29	.750
$1 Loon	2005 to date	7.00	.925	6.48	.208
$2	2004	8.8	.925	8.14	.262
$3	2006	11.72	.925	10.84	.349
$4	2007-2009	15.87	.9999	15.87	.510
$5	1973-1976	24.30	.925	22.477	.723
$5 M.L.	1988 to date	31.04	.9999	31.1035	1.000
$5	2001	16.96	.925	15.69	.504
$5	2003, 2005	31.30	.9999	31.30	1.009
$5	2004, 2005, 2006	27.90	.9999	27.90	.897
$5	2005, 2006	25.20	.9999	25.20	.810
$8	2004	28.80	.925	26.64	.856
$8	2005	32.15	.9999	32.15	1.034
$8	2007	36.10	.9999	36.10	1.161
$10	1973-1976	46.60	.925	44.955	1.445
$10	2005-2006	25.18	.9999	25.18	.809
$15	1992, 1998-2009	33.63	.925	31.11	1.000
$20	1985-1988	34.07	.925	31.549	1.000
$20	1990 to date	31.10	.925	29.80	.958
$25	1985-1988	34.07	.925	31.51	1.013
$25	1990-2003	31.10	.925	28.77	.925
$25	2003-2009	31.39	.9999	31.39	1.010
$25	2007-2009	27.78	.925	30.03	.966
$30	2005-2009	31.50	.925	29.14	.937
$50	2006	156.36	.9999	156.36	5.028
$250	2007-2009	1000.00	.9999	1000.00	32.150